IN OUR WRITE MINDS

William Scott MacKay
1931 – 2007

It is in the nature of groups, such as Sutherland Writers, that members come and go. For a group like ours to survive, however, there must be a central core of staunch enthusiasts. When Willie MacKay died, we lost one of our core – a founder member and an inspiration.

We respectfully dedicate this collection to his memory.

Included are some of Willie's pieces, but it is impossible in a few samples to give a worthy flavour of his lifetime of writing. He wrote stories and poems and rhymes. He invited us to join him in his awed admiration of a thing of beauty; to share his chuckles when he poked fun at pomposity and hypocrisy. He rejoiced in the community about him and found inspiration in abundance in the otherwise mundane and droll; which he approached with wit and mischief, and turned into a delight. For his great gift was humour.

As a group, we luxuriated in his couthy company, rollicked with laughter at his fun and warmed ourselves in the glow of his friendship.

We likely took him for granted. He was always there and we expected to be entertained; and we were never disappointed. But then he was taken ill and we had an empty space – one that had so recently overflowed with Willie. Hope of his return perished and we said our goodbyes.

We remember him with affection, admiration and, above all, with smiles.

Bill MacKenzie

First published in 2009
by Sutherland Writers' Group

ISBN: 978-0-9552505-1-4

Cover design by Charlie Byron

Produced by The Northern Times, Golspie

CONTENTS

FOREWORD

'Sutherland' is, perhaps surprisingly, 'the south land' – probably named by the Vikings of Orkney. It's a special place, vast and spacious with wide skyscapes, dramatic scenery and small towns of character dotted along the eastern coastal strip. It's a land of farming, crofting and traditional sporting estates; fishing and forestry; and, of course, tourism. Sutherland's history has involved a great deal of hardship, hard work, cruelty and sadness; as well as pride and achievement.

So, naturally, it's a place of stories.

The writers of any particular place are its bards, chroniclers, storytellers and creative literary artists. They record, evoke, celebrate and mourn; with their neighbours, and for them. In poetry and prose, fiction and memoir, they write of laughter and sadness and joy and loss. The wider public may not always realise it, but we need our writers.

Sutherland is fortunate in having an active and lively Writers' Group with a talented and versatile membership. I've been privileged to share one of their meetings with them. Some are mainly poets, others write chiefly fiction – whether short stories or novels – and still others write mainly memoirs and other non-fiction. Their ages vary and some are natives, while others have migrated to Sutherland from far and wide – a welcome reversal of the county's history of outward migration. They're all different, but each draws on his or her own experience and imagination to tell part of their story; part of Sutherland's story. This anthology captures Sutherland Writers *in their write minds*.

If you want to get to know a place, you could do much worse than read the work of its writers. Welcome to Sutherland.

David McVey

A Taste of Scotland

W S MacKay

The taste of Scotland is not something new,
Tartan-edged menus, *à la carte*, *Ecosse Nouveau*,
Smoked salmon, lobster, and venison stew,
All washed down with a fine amber brew.

The taste at my Granny's was different by far,
It was crowdie on bannocks, and milk from a jar,
Salt herring and tatties, mashed neaps and kale,
With a drink of spring water out of a pail.

There was dry salted cod that hung on the door,
A bag of oatmeal that stood on the floor,
For porridge and brose and girdle oat cakes,
We never got *Frosties* or packets of flakes.

A big pan of broth, boiled on a bone,
Fresh home-made butter on a newly-baked scone,
Bramble jam with the top of the cream,
So clear in my memory, now I only can dream.

The aye-boiling kettle that hung on the hook,
The clean white-washed alcove that housed the Good Book,
Her kitchen a haven against worldly ways,
There was my refuge in the Spring of my days.

The peats were stacked high at the back of the barn,
In the evening, the carding and spinning of yarn,
With stories old, in word and in song,
It was there that I learned the paths, right from wrong.

It's a Matter of Choice

W S MacKay

The wife and I decided we would do the grand tour of the North and West Highlands; our own country is hard to beat for scenery when the weather is favourable.

It had the promise of being a nice weekend, so we packed our bags and set off to rove where the fancy took us.

We knew that most of the arty-crafty shops and tea-rooms in the area were owned by people from the South, attracted here by the generous grants from *CASE*, *RACE*, and other sources of freebie money; most are nice, although more than a little over-priced. We stopped at one recently, a converted croft house, now a restaurant and B&B establishment, and here we had a totally new experience.

Greeted 'Good morning' at the door by a smiling landlady, I return the greeting and ask, 'May we have two teas, please?'

'Certainly; where would you like to sit? By the window, or by the wall?'

'By the window, I think.'

'Upstairs or down?'

'Down, please.'

'Smoking or non-smoking?'

'Non smoking, please.'

'Just tea, or would you like a meal?'

'Just tea, please.'

'What kind of tea would you like? We have *Earl Grey*, *Brodies*, *Assam*, *Darjeeling*, *Punjabi*, *Ceylon*, and *China Green*. We also make a nice peppermint, from our own herbs. Or how about iced-lemon?' By now, the notion had left me, so I let the wife choose; she made the mistake to ask for scones. 'Brown or white?'

'Brown, please.'

'In brown, we have wholemeal, bran, oat-flake, rye, half-rye. In white, we have bleached and unbleached, and all our flour is stone-ground by a friend of ours in Yorkshire. We also make a peas-meal cob.'

'Plain white, please, with butter and jam.'

'Butter, *Flora,* or the house-spread?'

'Butter, please,' I shudder to think what the house-spread was made from, 'and blackberry jam.' The wife got the preferred jam in before we got the list of preserves, jams, jellies and honey *etc.* We were not out of the wood yet; she came back to inquire if we wanted 'pouring cream, or full cream, semi-skimmed or skimmed milk. Or just black tea?'

When the tea eventually came, it was insipid, barely warm, and the scones were as hard as a brick and went to crumbs in your mouth, like grains of sand. But

I tell you, there was nothing organic about the bill; it was definitely genetically-modified for rapid growth.

By now, I only wanted to get on the road again to somewhere with a pub, a buxom barmaid, and a list of ales well known nationwide. That place has put me right against tea forever. One wonders if this is really the kind of service tourists expect; or if they would prefer the traditional Highland stroupach like Granny used to make.

Temptation

W S MacKay

It's better than the honey,
On the fabled honeymoon.
It's better than warm sunshine,
That comes flooding in the room.

Everybody likes it,
Some say it is a sin;
We've all been seduced,
And willingly give in.

We strip away the wrap,
Admire the lace and frills.
But cannot wait to savour,
The sensuous exotic thrills.

We caress each shapely mould,
As it lies exposed in wait.
Which delight to try first?
Sets our mind a state.

Some like it by the fire,
When the kids are not about;
Some like it in the bedroom,
With all the lights switched out.

Some have it every night,
And some just once a week;
Some only have it once a year,
At Christmas, so to speak.

But when the passion is all spent,
And there's nothing left within;
It's just an empty chocolate box,
That's ready for the bin.

Christmas House

Lynn Whittington

I remember having been to the house on two occasions; I must have been about nine or ten. Hard to remember exactly, as it seems so long ago now. However, it was during the time my mum's latest idea for making money was to provide services for the rich people who owned the big houses and the estates further up the strath towards the North West. There were only two types of people who lived in the strath in those days – the rich and privileged, and the rest. Those like my family who struggled to make ends meet; farming, fishing, forestry, fixing up stuff – the F work my mum had called it. And when you had been left a very young widow with a bairn to bring up alone, she used to joke that she would do anything for money except for the F work.

That was why she had decided to try her hand at laundry. Well, laundry didn't really fully describe the services my mum would offer. She specialised in stain-removal and pressing for finer fabrics. Which was why that Christmas our little cottage looked bright and cheery inside, with floaty-fabric gowns hanging from every available hook, dress shirts with their collars and lace fronts stiffly-starched standing to attention all around the kitchen, and brightly coloured waistcoats and cummerbunds glistening from the steam cleaning they'd received. Mum also specialised in kilts. Their tartans would stand out clear and bright, run through with precision pleating so sharp you could almost cut your finger on it. Yes, mum's services were in great demand from the party-goers, lots of whom were visiting the Highlands for the first time, staying in what had now become second homes for the rich and privileged.

Mum had done very well for herself finding a niche in the market. Christmas was very busy, followed by Burns night, then weekend parties for the hunting. In the summer there would be ball gowns to repair and press too, then back into the fishing and hunting season. Mum was never going to be able to earn a fortune, but it kept the wolf from the door and her in tales of the great and the good; of how the hemming in Lady Barbara's dress was so poor she'd left her whole wardrobe with mum to finish off; of how the Laird of somewhere or other had asked her to repair the kilt originally worn by his grandfather, and how she had made such a good job of it that he paid her handsomely and an article had been written in a national newspaper.

Of course, one of the drawbacks was having to live in a steamy environment, condensation continually misting all the windows and glass in the cottage. And my own clothes had always taken second place to those of her customers. So much so, that I can remember one winter when the seam on my coat had remained split from October to February before she'd found time to fit in my repair. How the cruel winds had whistled around my waist for all that time; until I had the bright idea of using my scarf as a belt – which did the trick for a while.

So why was I thinking of Christmas House? I guess coming home for the holidays always brought back memories, especially of the days when it had just been the two of us; *BC* as mum and I referred to them – *before Callum*. Callum was now my stepfather and the two of them still lived in the house I had been brought up in. Of course, Callum had seen to all the repairs and had commissioned extension work, building upwards and opening out the loft area; then outwards with a large dining room and conservatory, looking westwards along the strath and catching all of the evening light in summer.

The first time we had been invited up to Christmas House was so exciting. I had told all of my friends in school that I was going up *for supper* before church on Christmas Eve. Mum had made me a dress from some old cord material left over from repairing some huntsman's breeches. It was lovat green but, to dress it up, she'd edged the collar with dark green velvet; and it tied up at the back with a large velvet bow. I had never seen such a beautiful dress in my life and had been sleeping with it hung over my wardrobe door for the previous two weeks – so that it could be the last thing I saw at night and the first thing I would see on waking.

Of course, I was ready at least an hour too early for the supper. Mum had been up to the house already to drop off clothes for the grand parties planned during the course of Christmas and the New Year, and when she came back, I barraged her with a stream of questions. 'How many will be going? Are there any other little girls like me? Are their dresses as pretty as mine? What kind of food is there?'

'*Whysht!*' my mum scolded at last. 'You'll see for yourself soon enough!'

Christmas House stood shielded from the road and the biting winds by a large wood, Christmas Wood. The Forestry had, of course, planted all of the new growth but the original trees still remained in the thick of it. Gnarled trunks and twisted branches which creaked and snapped in the wind; whose aged roots cut through the drive up to the house and threatened to trip you up if you strayed off the path. As we climbed the snowy incline, I danced with delight as the twinkling lights of the house came into view. A grand tree adorned one of the two bay windows at the front of the house and cast multi-coloured circles of light on the snow outside. I could hear laughter and music from within and dragged mum the few feet further, so as not to lose any precious time being outside the house.

The interior was warm and welcoming, holly and other greenery festooned in spirals all the way up the banister on the stairway. Paper garlands streamed across the high ceilings and silvery stars hung from pictures and doorframes. It was so perfect, a dream come true. I remember how mum had flushed when the lady of the house, Fiona McDermott, had welcomed us to her home. There was dancing in the other front room, the one without the tree; pipes and fiddles dizzying my thoughts, as I followed mum into the dining room for supper. For weeks I'd been wondering exactly what supper was; now I knew it all – pastries filled with pinks and greens, a whole salmon glazed, with the head still in place; tiny sandwiches, dishes piping-hot with steaming potatoes and rice dishes, speckled with colour from foreign spices. A ham, part-carved with its juices trickling over the plate. And, oh, what cakes; hundreds of them sparkling with silver balls and frosted icing; some with fruit toppings others with cream. I didn't know where to start. Mum gave me a plate and told me not to eat too quickly or I would be sick all over my lovely dress. A couple of boys not much older than me had arrived at the table, so I decided I would take my lead from them. They delicately piled meat and pastries onto their plates, giggling behind their hands, as they knew I was watching them.

Suddenly, they were joined by a girl. She was taller than them, with long fair hair and bright green eyes. Her dress was so gorgeous; it was sea blue with lace and frills and ribbons that matched those in her hair. I could feel that my mouth had fallen open as I stared at her, but there was nothing I could do about it. She beckoned them into a huddle and I could see their shoulders shaking with laughter. I busied myself with a pastry and looked round for mum. All at once, the children turned back to me; the girl wore a horrible sneer across her face, which spoilt her pretty features. One of the boys then reached for the salmon, scooped out its eye and threw it at me. In horror, as I attempted to brush it off my dress, I succeeded only in rubbing it further into the cord tramways; its horrible fishy smell pervading my clothes and hands. Fighting back the tears, I looked across to where the boy had been – but he had fled, leaving only the horrible girl with a triumphant smirk on her face.

At that moment, mum came back. 'Oh, Mairhi, I can't leave you alone for a minute, can I? What a mess you've made of your lovely new dress.'

It was hopeless to try to tell her the truth. Who would have believed me? The boys had gone and only a sweetly-smiling, pretty child remained at the table, fawning now in the praise being bestowed on her for her good looks and delightful table manners.

When mum was invited back the following year, I really didn't want to go. But mum insisted. She seemed terribly keen to go and had even made herself a new dress for the occasion; a beautiful dark-red taffeta gown that fitted tightly across the top, then flared out at the skirt. She'd edged it with tartan and made a cummerbund – also of tartan – to accentuate her trim waist. I thought she looked like a film star. 'And I've made this for you,' she coaxed gently, as she handed me a coat hanger draped with a sheet so that I could not see what was underneath it. I pulled off the cover to reveal a floaty-pink dress. Its underskirt was the same red taffeta as my mum's dress, but she'd covered it with a shiny material that gave it a pink glow. It had capped sleeves and a sweetheart neckline. Now, *this* was a dress, if ever I had seen one; much prettier than the one that the horrid girl had worn last year and nobody was going to throw fish eyes at me in this.

As we hurried up the driveway through the snow that had been threatening all day, I felt the confidence in my mother's stride and let it flood through my own body. Once again the house was beautiful, with even more decoration and laughter if that was possible. We were again welcomed on arrival but, this time, a tall man accompanied Fiona McDermott. He looked very like her and she introduced him as Callum, her younger brother. He took mum's arm immediately and guided us through to the supper table. The other children were there already and I felt the glare of annoyance from the girl as she eyed my beautiful dress – much prettier than her own green number. The boys looked slightly abashed as they nodded to *uncle Callum*, as they addressed the man filling plates for mum and me. No, there would be no flinging of food this year; not while Callum was around.

I ate and ate of the delicious food, stopping only to swill things down with the lemonade and American cream soda. Then Callum asked me to dance. He whirled me around and around to a reel, until I could feel all the food clamouring to escape from my stomach; back through to where it had come, so to speak. I clasped my hand to my mouth and dashed out to find the toilet. When I eventually emerged, satisfied that both my dress and I were none the worse for the episode, the girl was waiting outside the bathroom door.

'Your mother's a cheap tart; my mother said so. She's dug her little claws into my uncle, but she'll have none of our house or fortune.' And she began to swirl saliva around in her mouth as if to spit at me. In shock and fear for my dress yet again, I did the first thing that came into my mind. I slapped her soundly across the cheek and she screamed sharply, the spit she had intended to launch at me dribbling down her chin.

Yes, I've often wondered whether that was technically *BC* or not. Neither mum nor Callum ever came clean about when they'd actually got together. Dr McDermott, Fiona's husband, had sold Christmas House the following year and I have never been there since.

We're having our own party this Christmas and the new dress I've bought is all crumpled across the rear seat now. But mum will be able to fix that. Mum's still a dab hand at fixing things up. Must have been all that F work she used to do – not that she likes you saying that, mind.

Needs Must

Mary Black

My man he was dead;
The foxes had fed
On my chickens abed;
They left not an egg.

'Oh my bairns!' I cried,
As I tried to hide
The fear inside;
I could not provide.

'But if one has bread,
Then we all have bread,'
My good neighbour said,
As my bairns she fed.

'Oh, your husband has died!'
All the mourners cried.
May the good Lord provide,
'Tis their gifts abide.

My young son walked ahead
Of the old wooden sled,
As it bore the dead
To his frost-hard bed.

Said the Factor aside,
'You cannot now bide
At the croft of *Burnside*
With no man to provide.

But come to my bed,
Your bairns will be fed.'
I asked, 'Will we be wed?'
'Nay, never,' he said;

'For my wife is inside,
She has ailed since a bride;
But has not yet died,
And so I am tied.'

A roof for our head,
To sleep on a bed;
To be shunned I would dread,
But 'All right,' I said.

Pecking Order

Marlene Cowie

He's a bully.
Blue-back green, grand.
Look at me.
Give me my space.
These back steps
Flow with food for only me.
Titbits tumbling from teeming pots;
a spilling pecking Paradise.
Maybe that's why
the blackbird sings.
He's a lover.
Cupid gives him music.
Who only knows which melody
will win her blackbird heart?
Is that, then, the reason why
the blackbird sings?
He's the daddee.
Proud to jostle
to feed his maw-mouthed bloodline.
Soon they too will trill their territory,
declaring with each note,
the name lives on.
Truth is, I don't know why
the blackbird sings.

The Hen

W S Mackay

I was in high spirits as I drove along the country road, on a long weekend away from the office. I'd paid the deposit on a hired car and made up my mind to stay bed and breakfast at croft houses, where the hospitality was legendary. I slipped a cassette into the stereo player, opened the sunroof, relaxed and let the world roll by. The road, as is the case in most of the West Highlands, was a narrow single track, which snaked its way across the moor from East to West. It had been used long before motorcars were around by the old drovers, on their way to the markets. Being so narrow, none but the foolhardy tried to overtake or pass; except at the passing places.

Unknown to me, about a mile or so farther on, Mrs MacIver was busying herself getting the hens' food ready. She called to her daughter, Fiona, 'Help feed the hens; call them in.' Fiona, home on holiday from college, was starting to get a little bored and was looking forward to the new term; and a return to student life. She looked at the hens scratching about in a field of stubble on the other side of the road, rattled her bucket, and called them, 'Here chookie, chookie, come and get it.' There was a scramble as a flock of hens, wings flapping, feet and claws flailing the air, cleared the dry-stone dyke in their rush to get at the food. Just then, I cruised round the bend at their croft and the last hen, a large white, took off from the top of the dyke. With a thud, it hit the windscreen, smack in the middle.

The windscreen shattered, the hen disappeared over the roof in a flurry of white feathers, like a blizzard of snow, and landed, kicking in the middle of the road behind. I swerved and hit the gatepost. The front of the car caved in, the bonnet sprung open, and a cloud of steam rose to the heavens.

Fiona screamed and dropped her bucket, and her mother came running out of the house. 'Oh my goodness! What has happened?' she exclaimed. 'Just look at my lovely hen!'

Fiona, regaining her composure, started to run towards the car. I tried to free myself, but could not get the door open, on account of it being jammed against the dyke. Sliding the sunroof back, I started to climb out, and ended up crawling over the rear of the car. I slipped and fell, right into the arms of Mrs MacIver who had just administered the *coup de grâce* to the unfortunate hen. She caught me in the crook of her free arm, and held aloft the departed bird. Overcome by shock, I passed out. The last thing I saw as my eyes closed was the silhouette of Mrs MacIver's head, black against the sky, merged with the outstretched wings of the dead bird; like one of the witches from Macbeth.

When I came round, I was indoors, lying on a sofa. Fiona plied a wet towel to my forehead. 'The car... is it bad?' I muttered, still in a bit of a daze. 'Can I drive it?'

'Och, no! It's all bashed in at the front,' Fiona replied. 'Mother has called the bobby; he is coming out to see what went wrong.'

'Wrong!' I said, regaining my voice. 'Your bloody hens, that's what went wrong! The car is wrecked and I will lose my fifty pounds deposit.' Before I could say another word, Fiona slapped another wet towel on my face.

'Don't worry about it,' she said. 'It was only a hen. Tomorrow it will be in the pot, and the company will aye get a new car from the insurance.'

Her mother came into the room and said, 'A neighbour is coming to pull your car out of the ditch with his tractor.'

I took the towel from my forehead, got up and made for the door. In the short time since the accident, the sun had gone, and a mist swirled around the high tops of the hills.

The car, a total wreck, was now in the yard behind the steading. I thanked the neighbour for his help; he was muttering something about boy-racers. I made to protest my innocence, but he just revved up the engine, and drowned out my voice. He turned the tractor into the road and, in a cloud of black exhaust fumes, was gone before I could say another word. The tractor had just cleared the yard when a police car drew in.

The local bobby, PC MacBain, got out, came over to me and asked me my name, and whether or not I was hurt; then he asked if I had been drinking. When I had convinced him I had not, and he had checked the documents were in order, he also implied that I must have been going too fast – at which I protested.

Just then, Mrs MacIver called, 'Come and have a cup of tea.'

The policeman said, 'I will take your statement inside.'

PC MacBain was near the end of his service in the Northern Constabulary. A bobby of the old school, he knew every person in the parish by their first name. Nothing happened on his patch that he could not put his finger on. He was respected by all; and feared by a few. Here, in this part of the Highlands, there were only two major crimes – poaching, by outsiders; and drink-driving. Although, the occasional fight in the local pub tended to liven things up. A widower, he had no family, and did not like to dwell for long on what he would do when he left the force.

After we had our tea, served with freshly-baked scones, PC MacBain quizzed me some more about the crash then, when he was satisfied, he said, 'Look, nobody's been hurt so, if you give Mrs MacIver the price of the hen, I am sure she will not press charges.' Turning to her, he asked, 'Will that be OK with you?' She replied with a nod. Turning back to me, he went on, 'You will do that, then. I will phone from the office and let the company know what has happened. They can organise a replacement car for you. It looks like you will have to get digs near at hand for tonight.' With that, he stood up, thanked Mrs MacIver for the tea and left. I followed him out into the yard and, as the car pulled away, I saw the parcel of scones on the back seat. Fiona joined me there in the yard. I don't know if it was cold, or delayed shock, but I started to shiver.

'Are you all right?' she asked, making it sound as if she really cared.

'Where will I get a bed and breakfast near here?' I asked. 'I must find somewhere to sleep tonight.'

'My mother has two rooms to let. I don't think they are both full, so I will ask her if you can have one.' So saying, she disappeared indoors and returned in a few moments with a big smile. At least I had somewhere to stay.

I collected my bags from the wrecked car and followed her into the house. The bedrooms were on the first floor, large and comfortably furnished. I sat on the bed, kicked off my shoes, and fell back against the pillow. 'What a mess,' I thought. 'Boy, have I been conned! I have to pay for an old hen, and it's not my fault.' A soft knock on the door made me sit up. The door opened and Fiona came in carrying a tea tray.

'We thought you might like a cup of tea,' she said. 'You can come down and watch the telly later, or maybe you would like to walk into the village for a drink. There is only the one pub, *The Ferry*. It's not far; just over the brae.' I really needed a drink, and said so. Then I thanked her for asking me. 'Great,' she replied. 'There will be a meal ready as soon as you have washed.' And with that, she closed the door.

I came downstairs to the most fantastic meal. Fresh-run salmon – poached – with salad and new potatoes from the garden.

'That was superb,' I said happily when I had finished. 'It sure beats McDonald's.'

'Oh did you stay with them last night?' asked Mrs MacIver.

Fiona smiled and gave me a little wink.

The *Ferry Boat Inn* turned out to be a lovely old staging inn and, although it had been refurbished, it had managed to retain the charm and atmosphere so often lost with renovations. The ferry, after which the pub was named, had ceased to run a long time before, when the bridge had been built. The old pier was now the divide in a busy harbour, separating the fishing boats from the pleasure craft that gathered during the sailing season. The bar was full of fishermen and yachting crews, with the sea and boats being a common talking point. The yachtsmen who called there were greeted as old friends, which was as good an excuse as any for another dram.

Fiona found us a couple of seats in a corner, while I got the drinks from the bar; then we settled down to enjoy the company and the friendly atmosphere. By the time the night drew to a close, I had found out quite a bit about Fiona and her family.

Her father, a crofter fisherman, had been drowned ten years ago, caught in a summer storm while hauling his lobster creels. She'd been only nine. Since then, her mother had been over-protective and was finding it hard to cut the apron strings. Fiona was in her second year at college and hoped to find a job in an office in Edinburgh. She had savoured her independence; enjoyed student life.

As we walked home, the night had a damp chill about it. The mist swirled low over the ground. Fiona put her arm through mine and said with a smile, 'That is real Scotch mist.' I felt a thrill at the closeness of her. She was very attractive and had a nice personality. As we walked through the mist, I slipped my arm around her. When we reached the gate, I stopped and turned to kiss her. She did not object, and hugged me close. Just then, an upstairs light went on.

Next morning at breakfast, I shared a table with an elderly couple; they were also on a bed and breakfast tour of the Highlands. Fiona was serving them and looked as fresh as a daisy; more than could be said for me. What with the drama of the day before, I felt quite hung-over. She put a plate of porridge and jug of milk in front of me, and said with a wink, 'You can put some sugar on it.'

Then I was served the most delicious, traditional Highland breakfast. I ate until I thought I would burst. No wonder the tourists sing the praises of the Highland landlady's bed and breakfast.

Later that morning, I asked Mrs MacIver if I could stay on for the weekend. As she had no bookings and the room was vacant, she was pleased to have me. PC MacBain came by to let me know that a replacement car was on its way. He stayed on for some time, chatting to Mrs MacIver in the kitchen. Fiona asked me if I would like to go into the village shopping with her. My heart flipped. All I really wanted was to be alone with her and she seemed happy in my company.

When we got back from our extended shopping trip, her mother was all-abuzz, preparing a meal. She told Fiona that Donald was coming to dinner that night. As I was the only guest in the house, dinner was to be served not in the guests' dining room but in the front room!

The meal was prepared to perfection and was served by Fiona. The menu, after a dram of fine single malt, was cock-a-leekie soup, followed by the hen with all the trimmings in a fabulous cream sauce. Clootie dumpling for pudding finished the meal, and another dram washed it all down. We all agreed with Donald when he said, 'She was a good hen.' I volunteered to help Fiona with the washing-up and, afterwards, she hinted that we should go for a walk. I needed no coaxing and, as we strolled through the warm summer evening, arms around each other, I thought that the weekend hadn't turned out too badly after all.

Fiona broke my train of thought by asking, 'Do you think Donald fancies my mother?'

I replied that I had not thought about it, but they seemed good friends. 'Your mother is quite attractive, so I bet there are a few around here who fancy her.'

Fiona shrugged her shoulders. 'Och, well, she could do worse. He will have a good pension.'

I was sorry to leave on Monday morning and promised Fiona I would write soon.

Back in the office, work had started on a new contract. Try as I would, I could not get a long weekend free to visit the north again; but we kept in touch by phone.

Then, one day, I had a call from Fiona. 'Guess what?' She said, excitedly. 'My mother and Donnie MacBain… they are getting married. And I am going to be bridesmaid. You are also invited. Do you think that you will get the time off?' I assured her that wild horses would not keep me away.

Friends and relations from far and wide turned out for the wedding. The bride looked radiant, but I only had eyes for Fiona. The reception was held in *The Ferry*.

After the feast and the usual speeches, toasts were drunk to the newly-weds. The floor was then cleared for dancing. The band struck up *The Hens March o'er the Midden*; and the grand march was led by the bride and groom, in time-honoured fashion, amid clapping and cheering.

Later, as I stood at the bar with Fiona and the newly-weds, Donald put his arm around my shoulder and said with a big smile, 'She was a good hen!'

For the last waltz, I took Fiona onto the floor and held her tight.

'We shall have the house all to ourselves tonight,' she whispered.

Then, as I danced with Fiona in my arms, with the night full of promise, I thought '*Ah, yes – she was a good hen!*'

The Concert

Bill MacKenzie

Putting on a concert? Short of acts? But you still want a full house? Easy! Go to the local primary school and rope in every kid with the slightest vestige of talent. Those who are left, you form into a choir. That way, you get every proud parent, all the siblings and a good percentage of Grannies and Granddads and aunties and uncles.

That was what they did when they put on a concert in the old Balnagown Hall in Ardgay and it worked every time.

First, of course, you booked your stars.

A concert would not be worth the name if it did not feature Davy Stag. He was a local postie, po-faced and sober; so it was all the more wonderful when he pranced onto the stage in his Harry Lauder guise with a crooked stick, a huge feather in his toorie and a distemper brush for a sporran.

Davy performed songs which he composed about local issues. Sometimes, he ruffled some feathers. His ditty about the church elders *who made a good week's wage when standing at the plate* did not go down well with the church elders. He had one about Colin Campbell's aeroplane, which contained dialogue between a passenger and Colin – in which the passenger enquired what those black things were on a distant road. The response was that, if they were moving, they were crows; but if they were stationary, they were County road men. That did not go a breeze with the road men or their wives. But happily for Davy, elders and road men were heavily outnumbered and we kids and other non-sophisticates cheered him till we were hoarse.

In our diet of fiddles and accordions, George Peat was a welcome change. When the big man ambled onto the stage, he put a shining saxophone to his lips and blew and blew us all away. Such novelty was received with rapturous clapping and foot stamping, and then George amazed us even further. He laid aside his sax, took a deep breath and sang. Not a baritone, or tenor softie voice, but a voice from the depths. We had all heard records of Paul Robeson, but we had never seen a real, live man who could produce such a voice. And his songs were about such strange things too; *Mud* and *Deep Rivers* among them.

Later, we were introduced to a man who had come all the way from Invergordon – a distant place then – so we weren't entirely surprised when he did such an outlandish thing as produce a saw and a bow, and proceed to produce magic music full of high, wavering notes; the like of which we had never heard before.

The rest of the offerings were left to the kids.

The first offering was the so-called choir. They had been coached by the school teacher and she had had enough sense to let them loose on well-worn old favourites with which the audience felt obliged to join in. The volume of the audience's contribution was enough to cover the choir's deficiencies. We had loads of kids who could carry a tune. Some could remember the words. But there was only a handful who could manage both.

Interspersed between the child singers, there were musicians and one brave lad who gave a recitation which did not make a lot of sense. I suspected that he got his verses mixed up. He denied it hotly on Monday when I casually mentioned it. A pair of podgy girls played fiddles. Their first rendering was a tune unknown to the audience, but we gave them credit for reaching the end at roughly the same time, and we roared our approval. Their second effort was their undoing, for it was vaguely recognised and their faults were cruelly exposed. The artists may have recognised this, for they picked up the pace and raced to the end. It didn't matter – they got a big cheer and left the stage blushing and giggling.

One of my class-mates did a turn on the accordion. The instrument was much bigger than he was and the only evidence we could trace that there was indeed a boy behind the accordion was two chubby hands and, above, two darting scared eyes and a thatch of red hair. He played fast tunes, but he played them slowly. That was accepted; we all knew that he was a learner.

One might assume from my uncomplimentary remarks about my fellow performers that I was a star turn. Not quite!

I was a chubby child with a shock of black hair, a tweed jacket which had fitted perfectly a year before, and a voice like an angel.

We all had two songs ready. There was no question of failing to be asked for an encore – if such had happened, we would have trundled out our second rendition anyway. My two songs were *The Isle of Mull* and a soppy pop of the time called *The Loveliest Night of the Year*. My Mum had said it was a daft song for a wee kid to sing, but she had been out-gunned by my two elder sisters.

Jessie on the piano was familiar with *The Isle of Mull*, but not the other. 'You just start off and I'll pick it up,' she said.

I was to sing *The Isle of Mull* first, so the worry about accompaniment could be shelved for a few minutes.

I stepped onto the stage, pale, trembling and on the verge of panic. Jessie played an encouraging introduction to *The Isle of Mull* and I took a deep breath and launched into *The Loveliest Night of the Year*.

Jessie ground to a halt after a few puzzled bars, but I had started so I was going to finish. My big sisters were beside my proud parents and they mouthed the words encouragingly, and I ploughed on unaccompanied to the end.

If the audience were puzzled, they showed no sign and, when the applause had subsided sufficiently, I flew into *The Isle of Mull* with fervour while Jessie, who had been surprised by my sudden start, tried to catch up.

'*The Isle of Mull is of Isles the fairest.*
Of ocean's gems 'tis the first and rarest.'

I can't remember what I did yesterday, but I can remember every word of those songs fifty years on. What joy! What relief! I bowed and grinned, bathed luxuriantly in the clapping and stamping. They loved me and I loved them. I sidled to the side of the stage, ducked round the curtain and went back to my seat, meeting on the way a pale-faced, sweating waif carrying a chanter.

Now I was free to enjoy the entertainment. Gone were the butterflies, dried up were the sweaty palms and, under the gaze of the dusty stags' heads, I could whoop and holler with the rest of the crowd.

It may not have been sophisticated. It probably wasn't even very good. But, by God, it was fun!

On a Prospect of Tai-Shan
(after Tu Fu)

Marlene Cowie

Now, first day of days,
I'm alive to you.
Regret won't erase
what you show is true;
whose unkind glare lights
lost tomorrow's flaws.
You're a gift which bides.
Your worth, a timely pause.

Autumn Feelings
(after Tu Fu)

Marlene Cowie

The very trees weep for me
And clouds hang low, enclosing
My grief which is now two seasons old.
Tied like the boat, my homesickness
Is tethered to nowhere.
Around me the preparations
Which I alone have time to stand back and watch.

Lament
(after Lui Che)

Marlene Cowie

I remember, remember, the sigh of silk
Gone from the bright yard, this yard now forlorn.
My lady won't walk here again,
Though her spirit roams the leaves.
My eyes acknowledge despair
But my soul is not yet ready to know.

The Test

Lily Byron

Iain's heart was thumping as he picked up his mobile and keyed in the number.

'Hello, my name is Iain Anderson. I'm looking for a Murdo Fraser.'

'Speaking,' said a soft voice at the other end.

'Well... eh... this is a bit difficult to say... but my mother always said you were my father.'

'What? Who *are* you? What did you say your mother's name was?'

'I didn't say. I just told you my name is Iain Anderson. My mother's name was Isobel Anderson. She said she met you when she was at Edinburgh University.'

'Oh, Isobel! I remember her well, but she didn't want anything to do with me in the end. I wanted to marry her, but she wouldn't hear of it. She said she was far too young. Where is she now?'

'She died three years ago, in Leeds.'

'Oh, never! She was too young to die. What happened?'

'It's a long story. Could I come to visit you sometime?'

'Well, I don't see why not. But I'm living in Skye. Where are you yourself?'

'I'm phoning from Inverness just now, but I live in Manchester.'

'It wouldn't take you long to come to Skye from Inverness, now that we have the bridge,' said Murdo. 'Have you a car?'

'Yes, and I have your address, if it's the right one.'

'In Broadford?'

'Yes, the Old Smithy House,' said Iain.

'That's the one,' said Murdo cheerfully. 'Are you coming the day?'

'I'd like to, if that's OK with you? Do you live alone?'

'No, no,' replied Murdo. 'I have a wife and two sons, aged fifteen and thirteen years.'

'Oh... it might be a bit of a shock to them. Maybe I'd better not come until you've....'

'Don't you worry about that, boy. You come. My wife knows fine that I've had a few girlfriends in my time and I don't think she'll be all that surprised,' said Murdo, laughing. 'She's very broad-minded.'

'But what about the boys? They...'

'*Eesht*... They'll be fine. Just you come over to see us. We'll be expecting you in about two hours.'

'OK. Thank you very much. Bye for now,' said Iain. 'Phew!' he said to himself, putting his mobile back in his pocket. 'What a stroke of luck! He might have been dead or have left the country.'

Iain couldn't wait to meet the man who was supposed to be his father. However, he didn't want to take too much for granted. That's why he had got the DNA test kit off the internet. In fact, that's what had given him the idea in the first place. One night, while browsing the net, he'd come across this site advertising DNA kits.

'Do you want to know who you really are? Do you want proof that you *are* the father of your partner's child? Would you like to prove that you are *not* the father of an unwanted child? Then send now for a DNA kit. A simple saliva swab will tell you *THE TRUTH*. Result usually available within three days!'

It seemed too easy, but Iain decided to buy one of these kits right away. He realised that he might never be able to trace the man his mother said was his father, but if he ever did, he would be able to find out the truth. 'And who knows?' thought Iain. 'We may have a lot in common and get on like a house on fire. If not, nothing lost.'

Iain sang as he drove through the stunning picture-postcard scenery to Broadford on the Isle of Skye. Murdo sounded cheerful and easy-going and Iain was sure they would get on together. Getting round to mentioning the DNA test was another matter. How on earth would he introduce the subject? Perhaps leave that for another day.

The welcome he received from Murdo and his wife, Sheila, was no less warm than he had anticipated.

'Come in, come in,' said Murdo, who answered his knock straightaway. 'You'll be Iain?' he said, putting out his hand to give him a firm handshake.

'Yes… pleased to meet you,' said Iain nervously.

Murdo, tall and grey-haired, wearing a well-worn boiler suit, brought him into their sitting room, where a good fire was burning in the grate.

'Sheila!' called Murdo. 'Come and meet our visitor!'

His wife, small and dark-haired, appeared from the adjoining kitchen, wiping her hands on a small towel.

'Hello,' she said shyly, shaking his hand. 'Would you like tea or coffee?'

Before Iain could answer, Murdo said, 'Give the man a dram for goodness sake, woman.'

'I'm sorry, I can't take alcohol. I'm driving,' said Iain, 'but I'd love a cup of tea.'

'Well, well,' said Murdo, 'fancy you turning up after all these years! Twenty-five, if my sums are right?'

'Yes,' said Iain. 'I was twenty-five in April.'

'I thought so. Your mother gave up her course at the university when she discovered she was pregnant. I was told she went to Glasgow, but I never heard a word from her since the day she left.' Iain made no comment. He was worried that Sheila might overhear their conversation. He wondered where the boys were. 'Did she ever marry?'

'Who? Oh, my mother? Yes, she got married when I was about three, I think. I have two sisters and a brother.'

'Oh, that's good. I hope he's a nice fellow,' smiled Murdo.

'Well, he was alright, I suppose. We didn't see an awful lot of him. He was a civil engineer and worked away from home a lot.'

'Is he still alive?' asked Murdo.

'I don't know, to be honest. As I said, he was away from home a lot and eventually my mother found out that he was having an affair with a woman in South Africa and threw him out!'

Murdo laughed heartily. 'I hope she wasn't maligning the poor man!'

'No. She found a diary with all his assignments with her – names of hotels and things.'

'Well, well, poor Isobel. I wouldn't have done the like o' that on her,' sighed Murdo, 'but...' his voice trailed off as Sheila came in, carrying a tray of tea and home-made scones.

'This is a surprise,' she said, 'but a nice one. I can't criticise Murdo, or indeed your mother either, because I had a child before I was married, too. Unfortunately, my little baby son only lived a few days. There's no hope of him ever turning up on his father's doorstep,' she said, wiping her eyes with her hankie.

'So he's told her already,' thought Iain. He didn't know what to say.

'Anyway, we're very pleased to see you,' added Sheila.

'Thank you,' said Iain.

Iain kept looking at Murdo for signs of a family likeness but, at present, couldn't see any. Of course, with Murdo's hair being grey, you couldn't tell what colour it had been, but it certainly didn't look as if he'd been red-headed like himself.

'The boys are out fishing,' said Murdo, 'but you'll meet them later.'

'You'll be staying for your tea, I hope?' asked Sheila.

'That's very kind of you but... I don't want to impose myself on you,' replied Iain.

'Don't be daft, boy,' said Murdo. 'Where would you get anything decent to eat about here, at this time of night? Of course you'll have your tea with us!'

'Now,' said Sheila, 'I have to go out for a wee while, so I'll leave you two to catch up on the last twenty-five years.'

'Catch up!' said Iain. 'We haven't begun!'

In the course of the next hour, Iain answered Murdo's questions about himself, his mother and his family, and was able to ask lots of things he'd always wanted know about his mother's life before his birth. Murdo was very easy to talk to. Eventually, they got on to more intimate topics and Murdo asked Iain why he had decided, at this point in his life, to find his father.

'Well, you may not believe this,' said Iain, 'but I was looking on the internet one night and came across a website advertising DNA testing kits.'

'Good Lord!' exclaimed Murdo. 'What next?'

'Anyway, that's what gave me the idea,' said Iain.

'And did you send for one of them kits?'

'I did.'

'Have you got it with you?' asked Murdo, his eyes lighting up.

'Yes,' said Iain sheepishly, 'but I didn't expect to use it!'

'Damn the bit!' said Murdo. 'I've heard of this DNA business, but I never believed ordinary folk could use it. What do you have to do?'

'I believe you just have to take a swab from inside the mouths of the people concerned.'

'And then what?' asked Murdo.

'Well, I think you have to send it away for analysis… but I haven't really looked at the instructions properly yet,' answered Iain.

'By Jove, let's do it now while the wife's out!' said Murdo. 'Just for a laugh!'

'A laugh!' thought Iain. What a strange thing to say! It was the most important thing in his life! However, he decided to keep his mouth shut.

'Don't look so serious, boy. It's not the end of the world. I'm pretty sure I'm your father but, whether the test works or not, you'll always be welcome here.' Iain wished he hadn't mentioned the test. It would have been nice to have enjoyed this first visit without having to worry about the likely outcome. 'Well, come on, lad. What's keeping you? Where is it? We'll have to be quick before the boys come home.'

'It's in the car. I'll go and get it.'

Iain was glad to be outside on his own for a few minutes. He had ruined the atmosphere, for himself anyway. Murdo didn't seem to be bothered. He searched in his holdall for the cardboard box containing the kit, which he hadn't even opened. He'd never expected to feel nervous about the whole procedure.

'You have it!' exclaimed Murdo. 'Quick! Open it up and let's see what we have to do!'

Iain opened the box, took out the instruction leaflet and handed it to Murdo, who grabbed it eagerly and began to read.

'Nothing to it, boy, according to this. We just do a swab each, put them in the sterile bags and post them to this address! Results usually within three days.'

'As easy as that?' questioned Iain, doubtfully.

'Aye, man, as easy as that! Well, let's get on with it.'

The procedure took only a few minutes and by the time they heard the boys' voices coming up the path, the whole package was sealed and ready for posting.

'Get rid of it, quick!' said Murdo, his face colouring.

'How? Where?' asked Iain.

'Put it back in your car!'

Iain met the two tall, teenage boys in the doorway as he went out. Both their faces registered some surprise, but they were used to people from the *Department of Agriculture* calling at the house, so meeting a strange man coming out of their front door didn't bother them for long.

'Who's that?' asked Donald, the younger boy.

'A friend,' replied Murdo. 'He'll be back in a minute.' When Iain came back in, Murdo introduced Iain as *the son of an old flame of his*. The boys laughed, thinking their father was joking. 'I'm telling you the truth. I fancied his mother something rotten when I was young, but she wasn't interested in an ignorant islander like me.'

Iain felt he should explain something about his visit.

'My mother used to talk about Murdo and I've always wanted to come to Skye and meet this man. I was in the area anyway, so I phoned and your parents asked me to call.'

The boys seemed quite pleased.

'Will you be staying for tea?' asked the older boy.

'Yes, he is,' said Murdo with a wink. 'In fact, why don't you stay for three or four days?'

Iain blushed. 'Oh, no. I couldn't. I have business to attend to.'

'Where? In Inverness?' asked Murdo.

'Yes… and the surrounding area,' replied Iain.

'How long would it take you?'

'Four or five days.'

'Well, come back here after that and we'll see what's what,' said Murdo. Donald and Angus looked puzzled. It was then that Iain remembered that he had put his own home address on the return label for the DNA samples. But he could easily change that when he got back to his hotel in Inverness. 'Did you catch anything?' asked Murdo.

Iain jumped, thinking of disease – AIDS *etc.*

'What?'

'Fish, I mean! I'm asking the boys,' laughed Murdo.

'Just one wee trout,' said Angus, 'not big enough to bother taking home.'

'If you knew hunger, boys, like your grandparents did when they were cleared from their crofts, you'd be glad of a wee trout, believe you me. It's a sin to waste food.'

'Och, for goodness' sake, dad. That happened long ago. Don't go on about it!' said Angus, frowning. Soon they heard Sheila coming in the back door and getting busy in the kitchen.

'You two go and give your mother a hand with setting the table,' said Murdo. They seemed to be glad of an excuse to escape.

'You're not going to tell them the truth about me, are you?' asked Iain.

26

'Not until we get the results!' laughed Murdo.

'That's good. I don't feel up to it tonight,' sighed Iain.

They all ate in the kitchen. Sheila produced a wholesome meal of haddock, mashed potatoes and peas.

'Is there no pudding, mam?' asked Donald.

'Well, we could heat up yesterday's rhubarb crumble in the microwave, I suppose,' said Sheila.

'Great!' said Murdo and the boys together.

After the meal, they all adjourned to the sitting room with cups of tea.

'What about a game of cards?' suggested Sheila.

It was years since Iain had played cards, but he thoroughly enjoyed the rounds of whist and gin rummy, played with the family.

'You might as well stay the night, Iain,' said Murdo.

'I'm very tempted,' said Iain, 'but I have an early start in the morning. I really should get back to Inverness tonight. I'll give you my mobile number, so you can get in touch with me if you like. I really have enjoyed my visit very much.'

'Stay, please, please,' said Donald. 'Mam and dad never play cards with us, unless we have visitors. They always say they are too busy.'

'Nonsense,' said Sheila. 'Don't listen to them, Iain. But we would like you to stay. We have enjoyed your company.'

'That's very kind of you to say so,' said Iain, 'but I really must go.'

'I hope you'll stay longer next time,' said Murdo.

'Yes, I will. Thank you very much for all your hospitality.'

The whole family walked him down to the gate, 'to see him off' as they said.

There was a glorious September sunset over the Cuillins and Iain thought how lucky they were to live in such a beautiful place. He could see them still waving to him, in the wing mirror, as he drove down the road and round the bend on the road to Kyleakin.

'My family,' he thought. 'I like them. I do hope they *are* mine.'

Back in his room at *The Palace Hotel* on the banks of the Ness, Iain opened the package as carefully as he could and withdrew the return envelope. Since he had no sticky labels, he just stroked out his Manchester address and wrote *c/o Murdo Fraser, The Old Smithy...* but his hand refused to continue writing.

'This is silly,' he said to himself. 'What if Sheila gets the package from the post?' They hadn't told her about the test. 'No, I'll address it to this hotel. Then I'll be the first to open it.'

He'd made such a mess of the scoring-out and re-addressing that he decided to ask the girl at reception for a new label.

'No problem,' she said. 'Will this do?' She tore a few from a roll of sticky labels.

Having re-addressed the return envelope and taped up the small package, which had a *Freepost* label, he decided to go out and find a post box. It was a pleasant evening and he felt the short walk along the banks of the river had done him good. He had a restless night, dreaming of family scenarios in Skye and having conversations with his mother who wasn't at all pleased about what he was doing. It was a relief to hear his alarm go off in the morning and to realise that the conversations with his mother couldn't have been real, as she was long since dead.

Each day he had to travel to different parts of the Highlands to visit businesses, on behalf of his firm. He didn't particularly enjoy being a salesman for ladies' knitwear, but it had its compensations. He did get to see different parts of the countryside and to meet interesting people.

One night he was obliged to book into a hotel in Wick, as it had been a long day and he had still to do some business in other parts of the far North the next morning. He phoned the hotel in Inverness to explain his absence, but asked them to keep his room as he would be back the next day.

'By the way, is there any mail for me?' he asked.

'Just a minute,' said the girl at the other end of the line. 'I'll check... Yes, there is,' she said.

'Is it a package?' he asked.

'No, it's a letter.'

'Oh! OK. Thanks.' Of course it would just be a letter! That's all that would be required to give him the results of the test.

It was late afternoon by the time he got back to Inverness and it was a man he hadn't seen before at reception.

'Keys for Room 23, please,' said Iain.

'Mr Smith?'

'No, Anderson.'

'Sorry, Room 23 is occupied. You'll have to take another room... if we have one,' he said gruffly.

'I'm sorry,' Iain said, 'but I did phone to explain. I would like to stay another three days, if possible.'

The man ignored him, tapping a few keys on a computer. At last, he looked up. 'Yes, there's a small room on the top floor,' he said. 'Not *en suite*, I'm afraid.'

'That's OK. By the way, I believe there's a letter for me,' said Iain.

The man tutted under his breath, as if to say *what next?* and searched half-heartedly in a box under the counter.

'Iain Anderson?' he enquired.

'That's me. Thank you very much. Could I have my room keys, please?'

The man sighed, then reluctantly handed over the keys. 'Room 42,' he said, making it sound like a punishment.

'What an attitude!' thought Iain. 'I wonder what's biting him?' Iain was trembling, as he ripped open the envelope.

'We are sorry to tell you that we will need another set of swabs to be absolutely sure of the result. Could you please send these as soon as possible?'

'Bugger!' said Iain. He decided to ring Murdo at once to tell him the disappointing news. By good fortune, it was the man himself who answered and, luckily, he was in the house on his own.

'Don't you worry about that, boy. There's no hurry. We have the whole of the rest of our lives... if we're spared,' he chortled. 'Come over again this weekend and we'll do another set of swabs. Maybe we'll make a better job of it next time! Then you and I can go out and have a dram together.'

'Thanks, that'll be great. You haven't told Sheila about the test, have you?'

'No, no. What would be the point? It will be time enough when the results come through.'

It seemed a long, dreary week to Iain, but happiness returned to him as he drove once again through the beautiful countryside to Skye on the Friday evening. It was growing quite autumnal now, with clear skies and a nip in the air. Best of all, the midgies, which had spoiled the summer evenings, had completely disappeared.

'We'll walk to the pub,' said Murdo, a few minutes after Iain had arrived. 'You can't risk taking the car these days. The bobbies around here are very keen on catching drunk drivers. They have nothing better to be doing on a Friday night.'

'Aw,' said Callum and Angus. 'We thought we would be playing cards with Iain.'

'Tomorrow, I promise,' said Iain.

'Dad says we're going fishing tomorrow – even Mam! We're taking a picnic,' said Angus.

'I'm not fishing,' said Sheila, 'but I am coming.'

'That sounds great,' said Iain. 'I'll look forward to that.'

The second visit was even more enjoyable than the first – not just because he stayed longer, but because Iain felt more and more part of the family. He really felt he belonged here and the family genuinely seemed to like him. He was reluctant to leave on the Sunday evening. He couldn't say when he would be back, as he would have to head south to Manchester on the Monday morning.

'I'll definitely be back,' he said, as he got into his car. 'Maybe sometime before Christmas.'

'Come for New Year. We'll show you a proper New Year; not a street party in Edinburgh, like you see on the television,' shouted Murdo.

They all stood at the gate waving, until he drove out of sight. Iain stopped at a post box on the way to his hotel in Inverness. This time he had put his

Manchester address on the return envelope.

'Phone me the minute you get the result,' Murdo had said to him before he left Skye.

'You bet,' Iain had replied.

It was a bit of a shock to hit the city again after his sojourn in the Highlands. He'd forgotten how noisy and smelly it was. His flat was just as he had left it – no break-ins; no plumbing problems; only a pile of mail, mostly junk, behind the door. It was amazing how quickly he re-adjusted to life in Manchester. His boss was pleased with the amount of orders he'd managed to secure on his travels; so work was going well. His social life consisted of going out with the lads for a pint and a game of pool at the weekend; occasionally joining them for a workout at the health club through the week.

Every day he was expecting the letter, but a whole week passed before it finally arrived. He'd got home from work early because it was Friday and spotted it amongst the pile of junk mail. He held it in his hand for a few moments, thinking about the family in Skye.

'Please, God, let it be what I want to hear,' he prayed. Then he thought, 'This isn't fair. Murdo and I should be opening this together. I'll ring him and open the letter while we're on the phone – that is, if he's at home.' He called the number. 'Murdo, is that you? It's Iain.'

'Hallo, Iain? Has it come?'

'Yes, I'm just opening it now. I'll read what it says.' Iain glanced at the letter. 'The DNA swabs you sent... *did not match*,' he whispered.

'What's that? I'm not hearing you. It's a bad line – you'll have to speak a bittie louder,' said Murdo.

'*They matched*,' lied Iain.

'I knew it!' squealed Murdo in delight. 'I just knew it the minute I saw you. You're the spitting image of my grandfather. You have the same red hair and the same blue eyes! What a celebration there'll be when you come for New Year! I'm off to break the news to Sheila and the boys! You will come, won't you?'

'Oh, yes. I'll come. Why wouldn't I?'

The Detective

Charlie Byron

Kribblebeg flipped his soggy fag-end in the gutter. I knew it was soggy because I examined it – being highly concerned in these matters, as becomes a detective – well, not fully confirmed as one; more in a state of becoming one.

I mean, you can't be one until you experience the thrill of investigation, discovery; to feel, touch, rub, scrape, look, listen.

All the great detectives are extraordinarily aware of everything. Not at all like ordinary mortals whose lives pass by without suspicions, enquiries, examinations, interrogations.

No hypersense, no tingling thrill when stealthily following in the tracks of a suspect. Only detectives find out what we are all up to. However, even the great ones require regular investigation.

Though starting at an early age, it was but recently that hypersense came upon me. Thus empowered, it was easy to make bold decisions.

Sensing that Kribblebeg was up to something, my suspicions led me to his dustbin, his doormat and the creaking un-oiled hinges of his letter box, through which, sniffing the stale air of his habitat, I found notes of decayed curry, diesel fuel and newly-stripped, old-varnished wallpaper. As evidence accrued, I was able to establish his favoured toothpaste, soap, fags, dog food and his nocturnal habits.

He was unemployed, perhaps unemployable.

As befits a detective, skill in the art of disguise is necessary to confuse others who might become suspicious; so, being conspicuously tall and thin, it was a little difficult to appear short and fat, but the challenge was met. Unfortunately, success was limited to brief periods during the hours of darkness, when opportunities arose to unbend my limbs.

Kribblebeg burnt the midnight oil, as his curtain-less window brightly proclaimed. He seemed unaware, or perhaps didn't care, that opposite was a flat-roofed building, conveniently placed to make my observations. Investigations revealed a way of access to the roof, by way of a fire escape.

On a pitch-dark night, I climbed to the roof and, while in the process of adjusting my telescope, heard footsteps ascending the fire escape. Someone had picked up my trail and was naturally seeking verification for his or her suspicions.

Hurriedly adopting my fat, short alter ego, bending my limbs up my wide baggy trousers and concealing the telescope, I pretended to be asleep. The intruder beamed his torch on my somnambulant form and peremptorily inquired as to my purpose, identity and status for being on a roof at midnight.

Standing up, I felt the telescope slide down my trouser leg. This caused alarm. With alacrity, he jumped aside, his torch moving to reveal his guise in the uniform of a constable. My explanation as an itinerant astronomer, despite my genuine enthusiasm for the subject and delivered in the carefully-prepared accent of a German professor, seemed to affect his respiration.

Inhaling deeply, he quietly and courteously bid me to follow him.

Sitting in a white, cell-like room, I pen these few notes, expectantly awaiting further interrogation.

Rooks' Hill
(Chapter One)

Judy Maker

'Sally, Sally, don't give up now! Please, we're nearly there; you've almost done it… Keep pushing; keep pushing… Just try again… You can do it… Please, Sally, don't give up!'

Sally was exhausted. The sweat on her brow was wiped away over and over again, as she tried to give birth to her first child; but she was beginning to look so pale. Annie wasn't sure that she could do any more to help Sally or the baby. It had been such a bad pregnancy, so many false starts, so much bleeding as she tried to hold on to her child throughout the waiting time. There had been illness in the whole family. Sally, with her frail body, had picked up all the colds and fevers; her young brothers had both had the croup; and their mother was rapidly reaching the end of her tether.

It seemed that fate had visited them with all the problems of life. None of the good things had been allowed to show their face in this house through this dismal year.

Her husband, Tom, had broken his leg after falling from a haystack. It was a bad break, with the bone snapping above the knee – and he had rolled about in agony, which had made it worse. While he had been on his bed, he had tried to move too much; as the break had not been clean, it was very difficult for Annie even with her experience. He was a big man and she had done her best to make a strong splint to help the leg heal; but even that was beginning to look doubtful. The colour didn't look very healthy and that did not bode well.

While Annie was trying to help Sally, she had realised that the baby was coming feet first. It was the worst possible way for a weak and tired woman to give birth and her strength was failing fast. At last, Annie was able to get hold of the baby's feet and gently draw it from its mother's womb. But it was blue. As Annie struggled to take the cord from the neck, she heard a gasp from Sally as she breathed her last. She had heard the death rattle many times. The child died moments later. Annie looked at these two souls and felt like weeping.

Betty, Sally's mother, was already in tears after such a heartbreaking time and simply couldn't face the work of cleaning the blood from her daughter's body. She was grieving from the moment her only daughter died and her grandchild didn't even begin to live. It was too much – too much all at once. Annie looked at the new baby and saw that it was a girl. She tenderly wrapped up the child that had never had the chance to breathe and put her on her mother's still-warm, but lifeless, body. She then got on with the task of clearing up all the cloths and rags, the bowls and the rest of the bedding, and then cleaned Sally's body and that of her child. It had been the worst happening of the last ten months and nothing seemed to go right.

Annie was tired as she left the house of sadness and she didn't look forward to her walk home and the trudge up Rooks' Hill to her cottage. She wasn't getting any younger and her old frame was struggling with the constant weariness of trying to live. She had been the village nurse, the doctor, the advisor and her many talents had also included caring for sick animals, as well as sick people. There was no-one to follow in her footsteps as she, herself, had been unable to have a child. Bill, her husband, had died in the first year of their marriage. The empty years were filled with caring for all the residents of the village. Her skill as a seer had not forewarned her of her husband's early demise, but she had always been able to tell others of good events and warnings to take extra care if the future looked grey for them. She had been able to ward off some of the bad times, but this year seemed to hold nothing but bad things that could not be held back.

As she was walking down the main street, she became aware of a lot of low mutterings as she was going by small groups of people. She couldn't quite make out what they were saying, but there were no friendly smiles, no friendly waves and the children were running not towards her, but away. This had been happening a lot more of late. She'd had the occasional grumble from people, but now she was beginning to feel uneasy. There was something in the manner of the folk; it seemed to be directed at her.

But why, she wondered? *Why?*

The whole county was in the middle of a potato blight. The summer had been extremely bad, as had spring. The ground was sodden. Due to lack of sunshine, the corn had grown very straggly and the icy mornings had added more problems. The rabbit population had eaten the fields almost bare of the crops that had managed to survive. The only good thing had been the explosion in the number of rabbits. Stew was plentiful, if you could find a few vegetables to add to it.

I wonder when it's going to end, thought Annie, as she neared her small cottage. It was halfway up Rooks' Hill, overshadowed by tall trees, and was the traditional structure with one door, two windows and a very thick, thatched roof, with a single chimney. She had been considering moving down the hill to be with everyone else, but she enjoyed her privacy. The wildlife was quite happy to be near the cottage, when she tended her small herb garden. At least that seemed to be doing very well. It was important to be able to grow all the ingredients for her herbal remedies, in addition to those growing in the wild. She had been so deep in thought that she was startled when Jack, her pet crow, landed on her shoulder with a loud caw.

'Hello, Jack,' she said with a smile. 'Give me some warning next time. It's a good thing I wasn't carrying any eggs. They'd have been well-scrambled by now, wouldn't they?' As she turned back from Jack, she saw that young Billy was next to her apple tree. 'Hey, Billy, get yourself away from that tree. I gave you one yesterday from my basket and there's none left on the tree. Get off home, you rascal, or I'll send the Devil himself after you.' She chuckled as he ran off into the trees. He was seventeen, but with the mind of an eight year old. His father was a brutal man and had beaten Billy too many times. There wasn't a bad bone in the boy's body really, but the children taunted him and called him Silly Billy. 'Oh well,' she said. 'There's still a smile or two left in me, even after a day like this.'

Jack had been knocked out of the nest by the other chicks, as he was the smallest; one of Mother Nature's ways of ensuring that only the fittest survived. Annie had found him with a twisted leg and reared him until he was as fit as the others – maybe more so. His leg had been put between two splints and she fed him with small pieces of rabbit. When he was strong enough, she taught him to fly by throwing him into the air and encouraging him to come to her for his food. It had worked well. He remained her friend, but lived with the other crows in the rookery. It had been there for many years and, quite naturally, the area became known as Rooks' Hill.

She opened her small gate and walked through the herb garden, checking the various plants on her way to the door. She was met by her cat, which wound himself around her ankles as Annie had been gone for many hours and he was hungry. So was Annie. She fed the cat and laid the fire. As it was coming to life, she went to the well and drew some water while there was still some light; to save herself the task in the morning. The fire was burning brightly when she came back in and she put a pan of soup on the grid. She checked her herbs on the string hanging from the rafters then, finally, sat down in her rocking chair after cutting some chunks of bread to dip in the soup when it was ready. She had been busy since the early hours of the morning when she had been called out to Sally.

What a sad time to go through for all concerned, she thought. It will be a terrible shock for Sally's husband when he comes back from the fields. He knew that the birth was so close, but he would come home to find two bodies, a grieving family and two graves to dig in the church cemetery. How on earth would he cope? As she had been thinking, the soup had come to the boil. She fetched her bowl and her bread, and settled down for the evening.

She had been dozing by the fire and woke to the sound of shouting coming up the hill. Male voices. Angry voices. What was going on? Annie went to her window. Moving the piece of netting, she looked out. They were coming towards her garden. Arms raised in threatening gestures. Flaring torches being shaken. Swearing and cursing. What is happening? Annie felt the cold worm of fear move in her stomach – a fear she had never before experienced.

'Annie Cooper, come on out here! Come out, or we'll drag you out! Come out, Annie Cooper! Come out!'

Annie fell to her knees and started to pray...

Quoyness Chambered Cairn
(Sanday, Orkney)

Harold Lane

Return, back five thousand years, when their children
clasped hands at white cumulus above their heads,
fast-flying over the charm of a wayward sea –
a song through time, as I, holding the blue to my breast,
search the sculptured tomb, a womb form, down
through the splay of the battered stone entrance,
down, down to their ancestral time piece
behind the night-shrouded constellations,
but by day still a glint of the sun
when she rises, rises over the sea.

And the sand, covering till from glaciers a little before
this time was set, above a foundation of flags
flat-fitted with care, as a landmark, a sentinel,
on the peninsula, fingering out between two bays.
I stand amazed, mind-set overturned, for here in the round
were a people building reverentially,
sculpturing stone with full awareness of place;
builders of the Divine holding space together
either side of tidal limits; with boldness
destined to fold this sacred shelf of land
to the outreach of timelessness. Origins set in stone
are retrieved from pulses in the paragraph
designated the Holocene – now at the point

where it transforms its geological back-pack
through a man-induced zone setting – the Anthropocene.

Undoubtedly, a New Age is calling, yet all this scaling-up of things,
this re-visioning through generations are truly
from the gentle Breath of the Divine Refiner,
Enlister of Messengers, Formulator of Intentions,
sweeping triumphant across the broad face of the Earth
into the heart structure of the soul of man.
'Oh, People of the Voice,' I discern the framework
of your Message, before 'The People of the Book' inherited it.
Each Revival of the Spirit propels our race forward,
slicing through Being to quarry forth Truth, the bedrock of the soul;
yet our pride has vaulted high above that Kingship,
as we depart from our quest; now we may retrace time
down the dark cairn's steps to these stark-coffined bones,
for theirs is a kingdom quite outside our show of things that fade.

Who can guide us, and how may we perceive
these worlds parallel with our own, these unknown regions,
that we were told when touched
may shine beyond our cosmic space of mind?
Assuredly, this Scheme is all-enwrapped within us,
as seas steadily billow high beyond our own wavering shores.
We may shutter down our wayward thoughts,
wander as the evening star strips time away,
or the sweep of aurora nights challenges our destiny
against the dull conventions of this age.
In our childhood or in our sleep may we still
clutch at cumulus just beyond our reach,
as the flocks of older times become the multitudes of today.

From these rhythms of entry and departure
appear such an expansion of the medium of heart and mind,
those perspectives of a multi-dimensional network, a flood
that cascades down through all reality, drawing life together
within the compass of a Universal Creative Force. It is here, here,
where the sacred enters through the unseen portals of the soul,
that the glory of place unfolds, strummed chords, rainbow-drenched
percolate their beauty into the fabric of times beyond our own,
as the music of times that are to come fashions the steel of our hope
through a vision of a newly-perceived emblem of Reality.

The End

Elizabeth Whyte

Death is the occasional gate-crasher, the sometimes longed-for friend and always a despicable thief.

He stole a child from my womb only days before she was due to draw breath. I don't know why I refer to death as *he*; it seems more appropriate somehow. A woman would never do a thing like that.

It's strange how we are so afraid of death, how we try to keep out of his way – all the time knowing the truth… that he will not be avoided. When James, my husband, was ill for so long, I think I was glad when death eventually visited. Perhaps *glad* is the wrong word; *relieved* may be better. That strong man wilted like a piece of old lettuce right in front of me. Death has no dignity; he waited until my man was yellow and sunken before he called. To me, he was an uninvited guest; but James just let him in. Death hung around the end of the bed for a few hours, and then he was gone, taking my James with him. But there, I suppose, he had a job to do. It was almost like a gate-crasher who stayed to do the washing-up. I never wanted him there, but he saved James a lot of bother in the end.

So now it's me who's waiting for him. I'm surprised every morning I wake up; I'm that bloody ancient! Existence is inevitable in this place, but living – *really* living – is impossible. The nurses trundle me outside from time to time; only when it's sunny, and only on Sundays. As you can imagine, I don't get out much!

On the occasions I do find myself in the great outdoors, memories invade my head. I can't seem to remember what I had for lunch – but I remember with the greatest clarity running with James through the new-mown hay. Fools we were. He always caught me; not that I was running very fast, of course. I think he knew I let him. The buttons on my blouse were of no trouble to him. I can't bloody well see them any more, let alone undo them! It troubled me that someone might see us, but James never worried. We laughed and kissed, then lay together in those humid summer evenings; our brown skin shining and the huge orange sun our only witness.

The nurses are good here; always so busy. Do you think they realise that I was young once? Oh, I know that they have seen the photos dotted around my room; but do they really relate me to that person? Once I was like them. My arms strong; my legs, too; and my breasts weren't just empty sacks, hanging against this rack of ribs. They were round and beautiful – so I was told, anyway; and not only by James! Are you shocked that, at one time, I was a fertile land; as juicy and ripe as a fat plum? The sad reality is that plums turn into prunes, given time. I'm living proof of that; but love has an everlasting flavour and, although I'm as dried up as an African riverbed, I still have that taste in my mouth. My heart has not aged; it's stayed full of hope and the courage of youth. However, the body's done for and my patience is running out. When will death come? I search for him in the shadows. He's never been one to walk in the light. Always slipping in the back door unexpected and unannounced. Pouncing with great gusto on the people we love the most. When you want him to come, he's dallying around, taking advantage of the young and the sickly. Still, I've got plenty of time to wait for him; only, this time, I think it would be more appropriate if he strode up the garden path and banged on the front door. He'd better knock loudly though – I wouldn't want to miss him!

The Escapologist

Simon George

For twenty years, he'd trod the boards;
his act, spot-lit; observed by hordes.
They'd come to watch, from directions four;
had queued all day, to get in the door.

For five years now he'd planned, the trick to end all tricks;
so great the illusion promised, in all the boxes, ticks.
His to be the greatest of disappearing acts;
hallway, aisles and seats – from front to back, all packed.

With shackles firm, his hands they'd tied;
then, curtain lowered – all bonds applied.
Unseen, he'd struggled hard; slipped chains from wrists now sore;
deciding this – his one true life – from him demanded more.

And as the curtain rose, he'd vanished from the room.
The crowd looked on, dumbfounded; sought him in the gloom.
And with him gone, it started – dissent becoming rife;
for them, the same bland future; for him, a brand new life.

And as I walk these Sutherland shores,
a free man, now – answering different laws –
I sense his ghost, shimmering close by me.
So, thanks, old Harry – Houdini.
I see it clear – they never *really* needed me…

Time to Spare

Wendy Davies

(Part One)

Well, this is it, Sam! Just you and me… All those years… Gone just like that!

Funny though, doesn't feel like I thought it would… thought I'd feel as high as a kite, but it's all a bit of a let down, really… Still, we'll just have to adjust, that's all. Once we've got into a little routine… we'll be alright. Take things a bit slower… That'll do the trick… All that rushing about… Still get up at the same time, though… can't change the habit of a lifetime… Well, you wouldn't like that. Wouldn't know where you were… would you? What is the time anyway? Let's have a look.

How about this then? *'P E Perks. In appreciation of 40 years of service.'*

Funny feeling, getting this watch… all a bit unreal! Still, they seemed to appreciate all my hard work.

7 o'clock… mm… would've been on the train now.

Still, to be honest… these last few years… what with all the changes… well, I felt as though I wasn't really keeping up. Felt sort of pushed to one side… things going over my head.

The thing is… that I was never the sort of chap to put myself forward. Just liked to feel that I was doing a job well. When promotion came up… well, I suppose… over the years, others were always there before me. So, I just sort of stayed at the same level… just plodded on… especially these last few years.

Of course, that's what Rose used to say she liked about me, 'I can always rely on you staying the same… dependable…' That's what she used to say. Pity she went like that. So sudden! She was so well! That's what I don't understand!

She had that little job, down at the school… every lunch time. Then, in the evenings, she used to sit and tell me what the little scamps had been up to.

We had to collect egg boxes, and margarine cartons. And, then, at Christmas time, all the wire coat hangers would disappear. That was the one thing she couldn't cope with… That Christmas play… Oh, she used to go and help… all hours she'd be down there. But she couldn't actually stay and watch… Always told them she was too busy that particular day. All those little ones all dressed up.

We never had kiddies, you see. It just never happened. Just one of those things. Some people have too many, and some don't have any. Nature's way, I suppose. Sometimes I used to wonder about it. But it wasn't a subject that people talked about then. Nowadays, well! Goodness me!

Anyway, like I said, she was so well! Then she got this pain, 'probably indigestion,' she said. But it must have been bad. Because she went along to the doctors, and when did she ever do that? They sent her for tests. And then she was waiting to see the specialist. Then the pain got worse, and she couldn't keep anything down. Well, I called the doctor. One Sunday it was. Oh, the fuss she made! 'Mustn't worry the doctor! Not on a Sunday!' Just as if there's only one of them. Anyway, he came... and... one look and a bit of a prod, and she was in hospital.

I could see she was bad... nasty colour!

I stayed until she was settled... They'd given her something for the pain... She was just drifting off... So I left quietly... Just squeezed her hand... And the next day... well, I could tell... when Sister asked me to step into her office. I hoped... maybe... she was going to tell me that the nurses were with Rose... But I knew really...

The little girl in the florist shop had done up a lovely bunch of flowers... spring flowers.

That reminds me, I've got those bulbs to plant... Nice of Elsie and her crew to think of me. I must get them a card to say *thank you*. I'll miss them... Still, we'll keep busy, eh, Sam? Plenty to do... This kitchen could do with a lick of paint... And that back bedroom needs sorting out!

(Part Two)

Phew, spitting feathers, Sam! Time for a cuppa I think...

Well, we made a good start, didn't we? Look at all these boxes! Some of them left over from Rose's mum, after she died. Maybe things Rose didn't want to get rid of.

Now, let's have a look and see what we've got... Some very old photos...

Goodness me, this one takes me back a bit! It's Rose in her nurse's rig... So young! She was a nurse, you see, in the war. We all had to do our bit. I stayed up in town, working in a munitions factory, and she was in a hospital in the Fen district. A big old house, somewhere out near Ely. Flat as a pancake all around there. Just a slither of land... and sky stretching forever. Her mother wanted her out of town, and she had an aunt who lived that way.

There were important air bases all along that coast. Still are! Handy, you see, for nipping across the channel. Towards the end of the war, a lot of Americans were based there. And they livened it up for the locals! More money than us you see, and no shortages. 'Over-paid, over-sexed, and over here!' That's what they used to say... Still, we were glad of them right enough.

Whenever I had a bit of leave, I used to go down there. I could always get a bed in the orderlies' quarters. The old *hot bed routine*. Someone who was on night-duty. I would like to have got closer to Rose, but the Nurses' Home was strictly out of bounds! Still, we had our moments! That's what it was like then, Sam. Every moment extra special! Because of the war. We had to snatch whatever time we could, and make every moment count. Because you never knew when it was all going to come to an end.

There was usually a dance, or a do on somewhere. And we used to walk home, laughing and hanging on to each other... and we'd stop awhile... And sometimes we'd lie and look up at the sky. And when the moon was up, we could see the planes going over. And we'd think of all the poor devils who were in for it. And we'd shiver and hold each other closer.

Of course, she couldn't always get away. And sometimes I'd spend an hour or two on the ward, helping out. There were a lot of injured airmen. Some badly burnt. Hands and faces. Blinded even! All bandaged up. So, of course, they needed help. With feeding... and just about everything else, as well.

And then there were the letters. Some needed help writing them. And those who couldn't see needed them read out. Wanted them read out-loud, over and over... until they knew them by heart... trying to feel that bit closer to their loved ones. Only kids, really. We were all just kids! A load of kids, fighting a man's war!

Now, what else have we got here? Some more snaps...

Rose, again – with some of the other nurses... And... here they all are in the grounds with some of the patients... And, hello! Who's this? An airman... looks like an American. Handsome-looking chap! In his uniform... and he's scrawled his name across the front of the photo... *Freddie*... Doesn't look like a patient... And... there's something written on the back... 'To my own English Rose...' *His* English Rose? Now, wait a minute...

There's a lot of letters here... some that Rose has written to her mother... And here's a little notebook... Ah, I see – it's a sort of journal...

> *11ᵗʰ May:*
> *'Thank goodness for Aunt Madge and Sylvia! I'm so lucky to have them close by, and they've been so good listening, when I've needed them. Day-off tomorrow. I can escape for the day, and see Sylvia! We can walk and talk. And listen to some music. And swap clothes. And laugh! And wear lipstick. And curl our hair. And try to be young again...'*

> *15ᵗʰ May:*
> *'Freddie in a bad way. Apparently, he was wandering around in the night, and found his way into one of the treatment rooms. He must have spotted his reflection in one of the glass cabinets, and decided to take a look. I don't know how he managed... all those bandages! One of the orderlies heard him sobbing...'*

Freddie? The one in the photograph? So, he *was* a patient.

18th May:
'Spent ages with him today, trying to get him to eat something. He's given up. Just lies there looking at the wall.

It started out as a beautiful day. And you were happy! Happy and scared! It was that heady mixture of fun and fear that you so loved. Up there in the sky... flying for your life! It was where you most wanted to be. But the sky darkened for you that day. Perhaps you were too happy! Too care-free! And your guard was down. Because you couldn't dodge out of the way. You just weren't quick enough. And he came at you from behind the sun. And sure enough you died that day. Up there, where you loved to be. And your soul is still there... floating with the clouds. And this person left here... is just an empty shell.

I can't bear to see him like this. When I think how he was. Thank God they are trying to get him out of here. Back home to his family. Let's hope that love can heal.'

Well, what do you make of that then, Sam? Was she sweet on him? He obviously cared for her. No happy ending for him, though... Still, what does it matter now? It's all history... and we were always happy! Let's call it a day, shall we?

(Part Three)

Hello, there's the post. Come on, Sam! Postmark *Ely*... Mm, haven't heard from them for a long time. Now let's see...

Dear Pete,
Sorry we haven't been in touch since the funeral. We suddenly thought about you the other day. There was an article in the local rag, about the old house. Apparently, they are opening it up for the public. Well, the old man died recently, and his son has taken over, and he's got a lot of new ideas. Trying to make it pay a bit, I expect. Anyway, it said that they have done up one room, in memory of the war, when it was a hospital. They are inviting anyone who was involved to a sort of reunion, on Remembrance Sunday. We were wondering if you would like to make the trip down, now that you have a bit of time to spare, and stay on for a couple of days.
Have a think about it, and let us know.
Lots of love,
Sylvia and Jack

Well I never, Sam… Funny how one thing leads to another. Just when we've been raking through all that old stuff. Well, maybe for old time's sake. And don't you worry! I'll only be gone a few days. I'll ask Janet next door to come in and feed you; and you know how she spoils you. You'll hardly know I've gone.

Remembrance Sunday…
'Here we are then, Pete. We'll leave you to it, and pick you up in about an hour.'

Following the service…
'Quite a good turnout, really. Nice address by the vicar…'
'Yes, indeed. Were you here in the war?'
'Well, my wife was down here and I used to visit… Of course, she wasn't my wife then. We were married in 1946. How about you, sir?'
'No, not me. My brother was stationed here. He was a pilot. Unfortunately, shot down. Spent some time here in the hospital. Allow me to introduce myself. Ben Franklin. How do you do?'
'Very pleased to meet you, sir! Peter Perks… Umm… did your brother… umm?'
'Oh no, he survived his injuries. He was badly burnt. His face in particular! Of course, being so young – just starting out, so to speak – it affected him badly. He was always so full of life. Loved the great outdoors. And he loved flying more than anything. When we joined you in the war, it was just as if it was the challenge that he'd been waiting for. And, of course, he had all the good looks… and the charm to go with it… When he was shot down, his whole life was shattered. He more or less gave up. They got him back home as soon as they could. But he never really recovered. Fortunately, the family has money. He saw all the best specialists. Over the years, he had plastic surgery. But he never regained his confidence. Not fully. They fixed his face. But they couldn't heal the scars inside… It's only in recent years that he was able to talk about the war. In fact, he wrote a book about it! This place… and the people he met…'
'A book?'
'Yes, a book. You may have heard of my brother – Frederick Franklin, the author? He recently died. He's written several best sellers!'
'Well, I'm not much of a reader…'
'It was something they told him to do you see… the specialists… after he came home. Write it all down. So that's what he did. Used to shut himself away. And he became quite proficient…'
'Frederick Franklin… *Freddie?*'
'That's right. That's what we all used to call him! Anyway, you may well come across the book, Mr Perks… It's called… Tribute to a Rose…'

43

The Spirit of Bogan Buidhe

Bill MacKenzie

Hey, old man! Are you lost?

Sorry, I didn't mean to startle you. Are you all right?

I don't see many people up here nowadays and with the mist coming in and the evening darkening I was worried about you. I watched you exploring the ruins of the cottage and wouldn't have interfered if you hadn't wandered over to this boggy place.

The well? Ah! So you are not a stranger here. Yes, this is where the old well was.

Your Granny's well? Now I have you. You were the lad who came here in the summer all those years ago. I remember you. Of course I remember your Granny better. She, after all, was here for over sixty years.

She came here when she married; had a brood of children before her man was killed by a tree he was felling in the wood. The kids grew up and left and then she stayed on here alone.

You were the last child here. You came for a few weeks in the summer and confused your Granny by expecting regular meals at regular times. You thought her catering very slapdash but she really did make an effort. When you were gone she returned to her usual way of eating when she was hungry and sleeping when she was tired. Clocks played an ever smaller place in her life the older she got. So did bed. In her last years she snoozed in her chair but she didn't go to bed.

Her fire was her constant occupation. Her every outing – alone or with you – down the road or through the wood was a wood-gathering expedition. What she could not carry home in one journey was piled beside the path to be collected later. There are still little caches of rotten, moss-covered wood waiting vainly for her return. When she found a fallen tree she would toddle home, like a little black partridge bobbing through the whin bushes, to fetch her axe and her bushman saw. Even when she was well into her eighties she would scamper home from the wood with long, heavy logs balanced on her scrawny shoulder. Tough she was, tough as a bunch of heather twigs.

And the well, of course. With two shining pails she scurried over here – cracking the ice to fill them in the winter – and carried them home filled to the brim, though the water was so clear that they looked to be empty.

That was your job when you were here. You never had to break the ice for you saw Bogan only in the summer. You carried the heavy pails home, resting often and often spilling most of the water into your boots.

And you took so long about it. Watching the scudding water beetles and the little yellow frogs, lulled by the hum of bees in the heather, the chirping, springing grass-hoppers and startled by the gaudy flash of a dragonfly, as big as a Spitfire – or so you thought. And seeing, looking back at you from the mirror of the well, a round freckled face with bright blue eyes and a mop of black hair.

But you stopped coming. Everyone stopped coming. No, don't look like that. I am not reproaching you. You all had lives of your own to lead and truly your Granny did not mind. She got letters from all over the world and those letters she treasured. And she had her fire and her well and her radio.

All day, and often all night, she listened to the radio. It was of little account to her what was on. She never got over the marvel that these strangers from so far away could talk to her and play music for her. In those days the British stations shut down at night, but that was no problem; she twiddled the knob and got Holland or Germany and listened as contentedly to them, though she could not understand a word.

When they found her dead, sitting in her chair, there was a smile on her face and her ear was cocked to a chattering Dutchman on Radio Hilversum.

It's getting dark and the mist is coming in. You will not find the well; it is long fallen-in and covered with moss and heather. Or is it, perhaps, not the well you seek? Is it the boy? The freckled face and the innocent blue eyes and the hair of jet?

Go home, old man. There is nothing here for you. The well is lost and the boy is gone. You may as well look for spring flowers in autumn or the glow of dawn in the twilight of evening.

Sutherland Revisited

Marlene Cowie

I was only a girl when I turned my back
on the mountains, with a sneer like the curve
of a granite rock; inflexible, I suffered no standards
other than my own. So I left.
Now only another exile
would know why

I returned to such a place. Unfamiliar,
longed-for. My mind tried to recreate
the illusion of past winters spent in such virgin snow.
Or were they? Landmarks under snow
were anonymous, uniform.
Strange in white.

The cold air of unease all around left me
aimless, limbfidget, for the first few days.
A draught, my lack of kinship, blew chill through each
open door. Until the thaw. With each trickle
of melting frost that dripped away,
politeness,

reserved for visitors, warmed by degrees
to a familiarity that saw no flaws
but stood yet on the edge of empty arguments that
spanned
my absent years. I tried to quell
the flow from ever-anxious aunties who
will rattle on forever with hollow fears
which they hold at bay with parchment kisses.
Every day I would thread this tapestry over, around.
Rejecting nothing, I wove each
voice and stone. Stoic Calvanist
sentiment

abhors gilding the lily; restraint is all
and spurns what is fancy for what is plain.
Kinship is the water at your roots, a secret
bond inhaled; like air invisible,
like air, an essential support.
Like the thaw

that revealed so much. Bracken returned once more,
ghosting a memory of long Sunday
afternoons spent walking, all paths focusing on the
bridge at the old mill where we would share a few laughs
with no thought

for the years to come. A close but distant place.
Kinship, I found, is not only the people;
it's their land.

'Do not turn your back on us,' said the mountains
to the girl long years ago when she left.
But there was an inner conflict which mountains
couldn't share.

A struggle for ascendancy.
To be insular or urbane.
Don't return.
Do return.
Was there ever a mountain yet that knew how to
forgive?

Waste Disposal

Mary Black

Gilchrist surveyed the banks of boxes reaching to ceiling height with a puzzled expression. There were well over two thousand of them, each containing the mortal remains of individuals going back over two thousand years. Either he had miscounted them or there were four extra. He expelled a sigh of frustration. He would have to start all over again and, this time, instead of counting fifty rows of ten *etc*, he would have to check the label on each individual box against the catalogue. On the bright side, it meant hours of useful overtime pay. On the not so bright side, the curator was blaming him for the discrepancy. He worked until nine that night, leaving a post-it stuck to the box he had finished at – so that he would know where to begin the following morning. After days of this boring pastime, he was about to tick off a catalogue number when he realised that there already was a tick against it. Someone must have labelled a box wrongly. Thank goodness he could now prove that it wasn't his fault. He continued his task until he had all four duplicated labels, then removed the eight boxes and returned them to the lab for reassessment, smiling smugly as he handed them over. He was dying to know how they were going to explain it. The lab assistants eyed him suspiciously, convinced that the error could not have occurred in their department; but soon their curiosity got the better of them and they got down to serious work. Later four skeletons were returned to their boxes and four were laid out on the examination tables.

'OK, Frank. Let's start with you. What are your initial findings?' the professor asked, looking grim.

Frank was green about the gills. 'Sinister to the say the least,' he said. 'Young; female. Died within the past five years as near as I can say at this point. Probably from a broken neck.' He indicated the damage on the skeleton.

'This one is male,' his colleague, Joe, said. 'About sixty years of age. There is a hole in the thorax and the bones have been treated with chemical.' Frank nodded. 'This one, too.'

Jim had a male in his forties with a caved-in skull.

The professor consulted the phone directory and called the local police station. 'Inspector Stewart is on his way,' he told them after a brief conversation. He pointed to the pathetic bone collection on his examining table. 'Female,' he said, his voice thick with emotion. 'About twelve years old. Decapitated.'

'Every bone in every box will have to be examined,' Inspector Stewart told the curator. 'But not by your staff. I'm bringing in a forensic team.' The curator wrung his hands in anxiety. Even after all his years on the force, Stewart had never actually seen anyone physically do that.

'Some of those bones are thousands of years old and very, very fragile,' the curator moaned.

'Well, some are only a few years old,' the Inspector replied. 'And we need to know who they are and how they got there. There is a child among them for God's sake.' His impatience was obvious. 'There could be more recent bones distributed among any number of boxes. Don't you want to know who put them there? Who had access? I need a complete list and I'm afraid that all of you will have to be interviewed at the station.'

They had to close the museum, of course, and every member of staff – from directors down to clerks, to security personnel and guides – became suspects.

Inspector Stewart knew that this was going to be a bitch of a job.

Morell was a mess. What the hell was he going to do now? The museum key and the order pad were lying on the table in front of him; absolutely useless; as was the equipment in the cellar – and there were two more stiffs in the van in the garage. Everything had to be got rid of. Well, that was his field of expertise, wasn't it? Making things disappear. He closed his eyes in despair. Once the discovery hit the headlines, the mob would be after him. He promised to make their victims vanish without a trace. He might have convinced them that the bones were the work of some serial killer and not the bodies that they gave him for disposal, but the kid was a dead give-away. He'd been really spooked by the head of that decapitated girl. Her eyes had been open and staring accusingly at him; but, hell, it wasn't him that had killed her. Even so, he could not forget the look of her and still had occasional nightmares. The poor kid had been in the wrong place at the wrong time and witnessed something she shouldn't. It only served to remind him of how ruthless they were and how they might punish inefficiency. He was paid a lot for his *waste disposal* services and the mob believed in value for money.

He'd worked hard to get that key and to steal the book of order forms. He'd had to romance that dumpy little tour guide and listen to her whine about having to take school brats around the museum. He'd had to convince her to let him in to the place. Had told her it was because he wanted to make love to her in the Queen's – God knows which one – bed, or on the Roman couch. It became increasingly difficult to be more and more inventive but, eventually, he got hold of a key and could let himself in and out in the middle of the night. He had watched dumpy Dora switch off the alarm system and memorised the code. He ordered chemicals in the name of the museum and picked them up in a disguised delivery van. He disguised himself, of course, for the chemical plant and darling Dora. Thankfully, she had no idea where he lived. He managed to give the impression that he was married to a bed-ridden invalid whom he could not hurt – but who had not long to live. It kept her from wanting to come to his house. Getting into the bone store was a doddle. To begin with, he just slipped an extra bone or two into boxes that had already been catalogued; preferably old ones covered in dust – but that was time-consuming and, occasionally, when he was pushed for time he just dumped a full skeleton into a new box, stuck a spare label on it, and buried it among the others. He was now paying for that piece of carelessness. There was only one thing for it. He would have to do a runner. Thankfully, he had an escape route already planned. He congratulated himself on his foresight. In the meantime, he had two bodies to process. He would have to do something absolutely crass like burying everything under his cellar floor and covering it with cement. Such a cliché – but there was no time for finesse. He worked solidly for twenty-four hours until the job was done. Then he drove the van out to an old quarry, stripped off the fake logo for burning and pushed the van into the water-filled excavation.

Four passports in different names – check. Cash, plenty – check. And details of bank accounts in four different countries – check. He wheeled his motorbike out of the garage. He had stolen it years ago, so he could safely abandon it at the airport. Out on the motorway, he started to imagine that he was being followed. He told himself to stop being paranoid. It was a motorway, for God's sake. Everyone was going in the same direction. He turned onto an underpass – and so did the car following him. That day, there was another victim added to the statistics of motorcycle accidents. Hit and run they said. Unfortunately, there was no ID on him and very little money.

The body count was going up daily. Twenty-three, so far. Inspector Stewart was sure there were lots more to come. Some were shot; some were garroted; some were stabbed; and some were hanged. The *MO* for each victim was different. Not one serial killer, then. Some had obviously been killed by professional assassins and others had just been crudely clobbered. It was a puzzle all right, and it was going to take a long, long time to get through all the boxes. They had odd bones and bits of skeletons that would have to be matched up. Like he said, a bitch of a job. The interviews were also taking too long, but WPC McPherson had come up with some interesting information from a guide called Dora Graham. McPherson had a chummy way of conducting interviews that made people want to confide in her. A lover whom Miss Graham had allowed access to the building after hours was just the sort of breakthrough they were looking for. Unfortunately, she could tell them very little about him. Just a general description of his looks; that he worked as a van driver; and that he was married. She looked shamefaced when she confessed to that last bit. Stewart and McPherson both felt that the naive young woman had been handed a line. They didn't hold out much hope that the name she gave them would be genuine, but they would process it through the system along with the description anyway. One never knew. In the end, he turned out to be the only feasible suspect. The fact that he hadn't turned up to see Dora since the discovery only compounded the suspicion.

It didn't take long for the investigation to show that more chemicals had been ordered than had been received at the museum, and a visit to the chemical plant produced a similar description to the one given by Dora. They confirmed the name Murray Cole and Stewart now had signed orders and receipts to work on.

Inspector Stewart had realised from the beginning that someone was disposing of bodies from different sources and on a grand scale. Obviously, there would be some key gangland figures involved among the victims and the killers. They needed to get their hands on Murray Cole before the mob did. What other methods of disposal had he used before he found the bone store? Cement boots in the river? Buried under the motorway? Maybe. But this fellow had shown more imagination than most. Nobody was perfect. There would have been mistakes, and Inspector Stewart – known as plod to his colleagues – would, with his methodical thoroughness, find them. With the help of Dora and a couple of warehouse workers from the chemical plant, the police artist produced a sketch that all three agreed on. Then they had them go through mug shots on the computer. On a hunch, Stewart had them shown only pictures of villains in the age group with the initials *MC*. Bingo! Murray Cole was Morell Crawford. Stewart never ceased to be amazed at the number of times people used the same initials when choosing an alias. It helped narrow things down for him. A search for the van was instigated and showed up mistake number two. It was found in a quarry frequently used by joy-riders to dump the cars they had stolen and was the first place the police looked when hunting stolen cars. An investigation of ferry ports and airports produced an unclaimed air ticket to Portugal in the name of Michael Chesney. A separate investigation from another area about an unidentified motorcycle road victim tied in with the time and location. Stewart was worried that they were too late and that Morell Crawford had died – and, with him, priceless information about the gang world. Fortunately, the body turned out to be that of a known villain with an established record for GBH. Not Crawford, but definitely significant.

Morell drove his assailant's car to the next town and left it in a multi-storey car park. That business with the bike had been too close to the airport. Plan B, then he thought and headed for the station and the Chunnel. The police were checking passports. No problem. His was a work of art; a real quality item. He handed it over, smiling confidently.

'Matthew Caldwell?'

'Yes?'

They cuffed him.

'You are under arrest.'

This Season's Must-Have Bag

Simon George

It's more difficult for guys, isn't it?

I mean, you might have an Aston – but that only works up to a point. Can't take it into the boardroom, can you? Otherwise, you've got to rely on watches, mobiles and PDAs; maybe a wi-fi laptop. Hoping your peers will see you've upgraded to the latest model. I suppose a few of you try to outshine one another with bespoke tailoring or understated *bling*, but there aren't many guys who can carry it off – at least, not of the heterosexual persuasion. Besides, how many straight guys can really tell the difference between a £200 and £2000 suit? Far better to be a girl. There's just so many other ways to make a meaningful statement.

Okay, lesson one. Listen in, guys…

Yeah, we know you'll notice the little black dress; nod approvingly at how it accentuates our curves; maybe find your eye drawn to the perfection of our legs. But that's all rather superficial. Who among us can't at least achieve that? No, what you'll miss are the *accessories*. Far too subtle for the limited powers of male observation. But trust me. Accessories are everything. Accessories maketh the woman. Take our shoes and bags. Even before the first chorus of *Here Come The Girls* has finished, our rivals will have checked us out; scrutinised every last detail the minute we enter the room. And it doesn't stop there. There'll be judgements about our worth – social, financial and moral. And did we do the season this year? What? Only made it to Ascot and Henley? *Oh dear*. That's us down in their estimation straight away. And were we invited to Paris; Milan? How many beau's arms did we grace? All of it leading to just one question…

Do we pose a threat?

Brace yourselves, guys. Sorry to be the messenger of bad news. But lesson one is this. Whatever you thought; whatever your mother told you… no, we don't dress to impress you; we're not here to make you look good; and forget any vain thoughts of eye-candy. We dress for one reason; and *one* alone – to outdo

51

everyone else. Doesn't matter if it's our best friend; acquaintances; or rivals. We'll try to outdo every one of them.

So, now you know that, you can appreciate the pressure we're under. 24/7. Why we take *so* long in the bathroom. Why we need our own cabinet. Why we need *all* the wardrobe space – and the drawers, too. Even though we're only at your place two nights a week.

And you thought we just had expensive taste!

Hey, looking this good takes time, money… and commitment. Take our jewellery – it's got to be designer; exclusivity *de rigeur*. And don't forget the perfume… You know, there's *even* snobbery over our tans. No, I'm not talking salons and creams – ugh, that's just *so* downmarket. I'm talking location. Location, location, location. Location's everything, isn't it? Villa in Tuscany? Oh, that's so *passé*. So last year. This year? Well, if you don't know by now, you *really* are out of touch. I'd give up now. Save yourself any further embarrassment.

And don't mention the gym. You think I enjoy it? Think of all the shopping I could be doing instead! Although… there is something about Vince. You know, my personal trainer? I'm sure I would have mentioned him before… No, now don't go getting jealous. It's all strictly professional.

But, listen, *none* of that's of any real importance. Not compared with what happened to me this summer. What?

Oh, only… the *ultimate* accolade.

One word.

Marchetto…

Yeah. And, do you know, I don't mind the blank face this time. It's what I'd expect. Thoroughly reassuring. And don't worry, even if you go ask a hundred women on Bond Street in the January sales, you'll get the same reaction. They won't have a clue either. Thank God. You see, Marchetto is *the* Designer Label of designer labels.

Think Holy Grail of Handbags.

Best-kept secret in the fashion industry. Even the well-heeled *fashionistas* think he's little more than an urban myth. To be fair, I did, too – until I was approached. You see, you can't buy his creations in the shops. Well, for a start, there aren't any shops. And, no, don't bother Googling him. There's no website. No e-mail. No telephone. No head office. Nothing. *Nada*.

You don't find Marchetto.

He finds *you*.

And you can't buy Marchetto.

He buys *you*.

That's no exaggeration. No, really – he does. Think of it like selling your soul to the devil. Or, rather – to the devil's *couturier*. Hell – even Satan's got to look good. There's this contract, see? God, I probably shouldn't even be telling you that! Well, look, keep it to yourself, okay? It's all very cloak and dagger. Anyway, someone contacts you… tells you you've been selected; you'll have done something noteworthy in Marchetto's eyes; and this is his way of saying thank you; giving you a reward. What? You want to know what I did? Oh, no; I can't tell you. No, really; *I can't*. Let's just say I'm not the selfish creature you've always taken me to be… So, Marchetto's added you to his list, yeah? And if you can keep quiet for six months, you'll be contacted again; receive your package. But it's *never* yours. That's made patently clear. It's all in the contract, see? What you get is only ever *on loan*. You sign on the dotted line. Literally. You guarantee to return the bag at a time of Marchetto's choosing. There's all sorts of terms and conditions – not that you're allowed a lawyer to go through them. But the promise; the *honour* – it's a no-brainer; of course you sign. Oh you wouldn't understand… but just to have had it… to have seen, *felt* the work of such a master craftsman; honestly, the feeling you get walking into a room… watching as the wave of ignorance sweeps across the faces of your inquisitors; knowing they'll *never* know. But you do. The satisfaction. You can see the mental cogs going round as they desperately try to figure it out. *Where* did you get it? More to the point, *what* is it? And *whose* is it? Drawing a blank each and every time. Ah, the *feeling*. That *boost* to your self-confidence. The wonder-bra of wellbeing. Honestly, there's nothing on earth can touch it.

You're still not getting it, are you?

Look – imagine all your birthdays rolled into one; all the girls you've ever loved; your team top of the league; the car you've always wanted; every fantasy you've ever had fulfilled. Now, multiply by ten. And again. Right, now you're getting there… and you can take that smile off your face… you're still in fantasy land, aren't you? But even then, you're still way off…

Trust me. It's a girl thing.

And do you know – well, this is what they told me – at any one time, there's only *ever* a hundred of Marchetto's creations out there. A hundred. In the *whole* world. Just think of that. That means I'm more important than… A-listers; actresses; royalty even. Just how *special* do you think that makes me feel?

What? You want to see it? Like I'd bring something that valuable here… Yeah, okay – you're right, I did. But, hey – don't look so smug. The day you think you know me, I'm off. Yeah, seriously… Why? Why did I risk it? Well, I guess its very exclusivity is its best protection. Ironic or what? Who's going to steal something they don't recognise? Alright, just wait. I'll get it. Give me a moment. It's here in the drawer.

But you know what?

Even after all I've said, I *would* actually be prepared to give it up. Means breaking the contract… but I'd take the risk; face the consequences. God, no – not for money. No… I'm thinking of something far more valuable.

Another bag.

Whose? No, you don't understand. There's no-one more exclusive than

Marchetto. I told you before. No-one. No, see... I'd trade his... *not* to have this other bag. What do you mean *what do I mean*? Don't you understand English? I thought you'd inherited the brains in your family? Just as well you've got money... Look, let me put it this way. You know when you get a present you don't really want? Well, yeah, I guess it's like when Hector got you those golf clubs; sort of... but, you know, you can't *not* be seen with it, yeah? Well, it's like that with me. I've been given this *other* bag. Not my style at all. Embarrassing, really – but I can't risk being seen without it. Why? Just can't, okay... No, that's a stupid idea – of course I can't just *lose* it somewhere convenient. You still haven't got it, have you? What did I ever see in you? Alright... Look, let me show you. That'll be easiest. No, it's not in the drawer... Just wait, yeah? Okay... here... *see*... God, I know. *Shocking*! So little design or thought went into this one. But it's a best-seller. No, really it is. Thousands all over the world... And I'm stuck with it. How long? Oh, it'll be several more months yet.

All because of the colostomy.

For me, now... this season's *must-have* bag...

Home to Roost

Lynn Whittington

'Jacek! Come out here! There's someone coming up from the river!'

The old woman had stopped feeding the scrawny chickens and was staring out towards the thicket, across the marshland from her village. Her husband came out at once for, although she was old, the woman still possessed remarkable sight. He stood next to her, pulling his worn coat about him as he felt the full force of the morning dampness.

A late autumn mist had crept up from the Vistula, kicked its heels half-heartedly about the trees, then gained courage over the marshy area before fizzling out at the outskirts of the village. The old man could see nothing. He coughed, once and hollow; then spat at the nearest chicken, sending it scuttling off into the mist. He muttered under his breath and turned to go back into the hut and the hissing samovar.

'No, look there!' She grabbed his arm and pointed towards the thicket. 'It's a rider, just the one,' she proclaimed proudly.

And she was right. As he stood and stared, letting his tired eyes become adjusted to the deceptive view, he was able to make out a movement; a large bulk, obviously someone on horseback.

'What on earth can it mean?' he questioned her. No-one ever visited the village unannounced or unexpected; let alone at this ungodly hour.

They waited; huddled together in the faint blanket of mist, as the uncaring chickens pecked and scratched around their feet.

The horse was pale in colour, probably light grey, for it would appear then disappear in the mist which was swirling and now slipping back towards its watery birth place. The rider was clad in some kind of dark garment. As the spectral animal approached, the old couple could hear the squelching and sloshing of hooves in the dank leafy mud.

'God greet you,' the figure spoke; a small feminine voice with traces of a Baltic accent.

'What do you want?' barked the old man. He was cold and hungry; yet another winter was threatening to sap his aging pitiful reserves and he did not need bother from a stranger.

'Is this not the village of Tuszcz? I am seeking only food and shelter for a while, and I am willing to work for both.' Her voice trailed away into the mist, devoid of any particular interest. The huge horse snuffled and tossed its head into the air, its frosty breaths indiscernible from the atmosphere.

'You'll not find work here,' said the old woman. 'Maybe someone'll spare a bite of food, but I doubt it. We certainly can't.' Her nod took in her husband, her chickens and her home; all her possessions in fact.

'That's a fine animal, where did you get it?' asked the old man, trying to approach the horse; laying a blue-tinged hand on the girl's garment.

Its eyes wild with fear, its nostrils quivering with disdain, the horse jerkily obeyed its rider's orders to move away through the mud.

'He's mine,' was all the small voice answered, as the horse and rider moved on up towards the village, leaving the old couple staring, mouths agape.

The village was barely awake as the girl rode into its centre. A couple of disinterested watch-dogs raised a sleepy eye or cocked a dirt-caked ear, but that was all. The simple, wooden homes were lit by warm fires to cater for the samovars – if the families were rich enough to own one. Otherwise, the breakfast would consist of hot water and a lump of sugar; maybe a little kasha or wheat-cake.

The girl reined her horse to a halt in the central square clearing and slithered down its strong muscular withers to the slimy brown earth. The animal, finely bred and sensitive, looked around himself with wide-opened frightened eyes before lowering his muzzle to the water trough to drink. The girl stood by, waiting.

The village seemed to come alive, as if by one accord; the older men emerging from the door of their huts like dreamers from a deep sleep. They even coughed in unison as the first outdoor breaths of air caught at their sleep-weary lungs. They appeared to catch sight of the girl at the same time, for slowly a circle of seven men formed around the strangers. Villagers are naturally suspicious but the girl and her horse were a strange vision to arise from the mists at this time of the morning. The girl, as if in complete indifference to their inane staring, freed her scraggy brown hair from the dark wrap, her glance cast down to her feet.

'What do you want here?' The question came from what appeared to be the eldest of the men. The others seemed braver too, as if now reassured by his boldness and authority; even the timid watch-dogs crept forward to join the circle, cowering behind their masters' legs.

She took a long time to answer. 'I would like to earn some food and a place to sleep for a while. I have travelled without a stop from Malkbork and we are both in need of some rest.' She nodded towards the horse.

The men glanced from one to another to the girl and to the frightened animal.

'My wife may give you a little wheat cake and tea if you were to help her collecting fire-wood. Perhaps you'll lend me that 'orse for the day?' The man who spoke was one of the older men; he rubbed his chin as he spoke, choosing his words with great deliberation.

'I'll lend him, but you'll not find him of any use. He only works for me,' the girl smiled as she replied.

'Huh,' was all the elder scoffed in answer, and he strode over to the animal, grabbing at the bridle. The horse screamed in fear and reared violently, striking out at the man with its forelegs. Again the man tried to approach, but the horse dropped its legs and wheeled about as if to kick him, snorting and squealing continuously.

'Calm him down!' yelled the outraged man, red and purple in the face.

The girl raised a frail hand to the quivering nostrils and the animal quietened down immediately, still glaring at the man.

'I told you,' she said plainly.

The men stood dumbfounded. The dogs crept back to their places and a strange quiet fell over the gathering.

'Which is your hut?' There was no trace of fear in her voice and her brave eyes held the elder's defiantly.

The village drifted slowly into its daily routine, the only exception being the strange young girl who was helping the women to collect wood for the winter fires. For two days she was allowed to stay in the shelter of the rough wooden hut that belonged to the elder and his family, but there was a prevailing uneasy quietness in the atmosphere.

It was not until the end of the third day, when a pink dusk had begun to settle over the collection of straggling huts, that the family, which had taken the stranger in, sat gathered around a crude wooden table to eat the evening meal. The wife of the elder had prepared wheat and rabbit stew with huge chunks of rough bread. The men, namely her husband and two sons, drank vodka; the girl drank kvass, eating like a bird.

'You'd best go tomorrow,' the wife announced quite suddenly. 'There'll not be enough food to go round for long… I'm sorry,' she added, almost as an afterthought.

The woman was unhappy and had felt strangely unsettled since the girl's arrival. It was not that she had anything against the girl herself, it was just that she didn't like strangers in general. She was afraid that any of the unhappy past would come to light again. She remembered a time when another stranger had arrived at the village; a young merchant, a handsome charmer who had wooed the isolated and often lonely women of the village with his youthful looks and masculine prowess. Many were the tales he had told of his life in the great cities of Krakow and Warsaw, and many were the hearts that were broken when he had left after a few weeks. Not least was the heart of the daughter of the elder, a young girl of no more than fifteen. But after several more weeks, it became apparent to the wife of the elder that her young daughter had even more to grieve about. The girl was sickly and lethargic; to her mother, quite obviously pregnant and a disgrace to any family – especially one of her father's standing amongst the villages.

The wife remembered how she had fought with her husband over his intention to banish the girl from his household, and how eventually she had lost. Late one windy, cold night their daughter had been packed off with some food and a little money; told never to return. The girl had never come back; no-one had ever heard of her since. To the whole village, the poor creature had drowned in a dreadful accident in the fast-flowing, treacherous river and, although the women suspected otherwise, to all of them – even her parents and her baby brothers – she was dead.

The wife cleared away the dishes and watched the girl uneasily as they all settled down to sleep. She would be glad when day came and the stranger would be gone from their lives.

The next day dawned cold and clear, a feeble sun filtering through the weak breeze, unable to warm the brown earth. Snow was heralded; it would not be long now. The families were sluggish and reluctant to leave the meagre warmth of their sparse huts. It was well into the morning before anyone stirred for working. The women busied themselves in their homes; mending clothes, re-stuffing mattresses, preparing food. The men took stock of the reserves of vodka and turned the piles of rotting potatoes. The girl had been banished from the hut with a large crust of moulding bread. She stood in the central clearing, feeding the bread to her horse; watching, seemingly waiting.

The day wore on into the afternoon; grey-white clouds massed on the far side of the river, preparing for a night attack. Still the girl watched and waited.

When the light faded, the horse and rider seemed suddenly to stir. The old woman who lived at the edge of the village was hurrying up towards the main group of huts, muffled in an old coat, panting and wheezing in distress. She pounded on the elder's hut. Immediately all the doors in the village opened…

the girl and the horse approached, waiting.

'It's Jacek!' The woman was sobbing, the elder holding her quivering shoulders. 'God have mercy on us all, but I'll swear 'tis the plague!' She broke down.

A stunned silence fell over the listeners. Of course, the plague was rife in the squalid cities; but out here in the fresh air of the countryside, it was inconceivable – unless… a *stranger*? They turned with one accord to the girl, but both she and the horse had gone.

The moon was not yet up as the girl tightened her robe around her thighs to keep out more of the cold. The horse strode purposefully towards the river, back to Malkbork. She half closed her eyes and allowed a sly smile to crease her dry lips. This was the journey her mother had taken years before, when she, too, had been sent away from the village. The girl warmed to the thought that, from now on, the village would be dead; not just to her – but even to the rest of the world.

Sanctuary for Cranes
(from *Thinkers and Dreamers*)

Harold Lane

It's Saturday mid-afternoon when Mark and Marina – married only the previous year – depart from their modest home in Trudovoye, just North of Vladivostok, in Marina's Mercedes. They travel 150 kilometres up the M60 to reach the Crane Sanctuary. Surprisingly, the car park is completely empty. They walk towards the entrance that is located within the Khorolsk Protected Area. It is such a strange structure, appearing to have been formed using a resurrected, prehistoric building technique; though, of course, this isn't intended. The archway at the entrance – open, without gate or doors – leads to a causeway that is over a kilometre long; its passage looming dark and foreboding, terminating at the visitors' hide.

The structure above ground – or rather, the huge bundles of branches and long twigs that rise far over marshy land – is open to the elements; acting as both roosting and nesting areas for the cranes; areas undisturbed by the presence of humans beneath them. The couple pass by a dull, red-painted metal box on a tubular post – meant to receive voluntary contributions – that has been broken into; they also pass a notice, carved from weathered Ayan spruce that has been fixed above the arch, naming the sanctuary and its authority, the Committee on Environmental Protection – known as *Zapovednik*; the authority responsible for its creation – with the completion date shown as September 2003. An overpowering smell is noticeable, even before they enter. Marina turns away and retches; Mark places his arms around her and, after a few moments, reassured, she shakes her head, looks up at Mark, trying for a smile.

Mark asks, 'Are you alright, dear; or shall we return home?'

Marina stares at him. 'No, not at all; I'm fine now. I came here to show you something very special, Mark, didn't I? I'm ready to go on now; sorry for all the fuss.'

They both gradually accustom themselves to the dreadful stench – an unrefined brew of bird droppings from various species – that feels sickening, unhygienic; and even the wind blowing through from above does not provide any relief. The damp floor seems to exacerbate the unpleasant odour, acting sponge-like; as a drainage medium for all things moist. Some light does enter between the branches, twigs and slakes of dried moss and lichen. These are shrouded in nylon netting, clipped to tightened stainless steel wire purlins that carry these heaps of brush-wood over rough-hewn timber trusses. Naturally, some of the timber has dislodged now, splinters spread around the wooden floor beneath. Mark is intrigued by its simplicity, but not at all by its effect. The side-walls of the passage, two metres high, are of stout lapped boarding, fixed to logs that are hammered deep into the soggy ground; while the causeway itself is built of heavy slats matted down with earth, set well above the marsh land – reminding Mark of pictures he has seen of the timber walkways within early-Medieval Russian fortified cities.

This windswept swamp is situated in the Primorsky Krai region of the Russian Far East, just South of Lake Khanka, between the Khorolsk and Spassky sectors.

There are signs fixed to the log posts that support the wall-cladding – red triangles, showing fingers in profile against lips, with words in Russian stating *Shh... do not disturb nesting birds above you*. They are clearly not above the couple now, as the birds are too busy foraging. Mark kicks an old, empty Vodka bottle with intent; passing it to Marina who, in black leather boots, kicks it back with ease; her eyes glinting naughtily as she announces, 'Shh...' with a giggle. And so the game continues for another two hundred metres. The two young people are in a boisterous mood.

Presently, Marina informs her husband, 'I wanted to bring you here, Mark – though I have never been before myself – to inspire you, so you can create for us those marvellous communities that your father once built in *Shhcotland*; with a real feel for living things, to build works of art fitting for our Russian Motherland. Besides, you would never see these cranes in your *Shhcottish* Highlands now, would you, my dear one?'

Marina is a tall girl of thirty, but who looks only about twenty. Wife and secretary to Mark, she is nevertheless more than that – the recognized liaison between the *Chastnik*, that is, Mark's consultancy in Primorsky Krai, and the internal security service, the FSB. She benefits from her father's legacy for, before his retirement, he was a prominent member of this arm of the law enforcement community. But of even greater importance is the fact she is known to – one might say feared by – lurking elements of banditry and other unseemly *ugolovniki,* the criminal elements in the region; elements that are wary of the scope of the FSB's operations here. Mark is exceedingly grateful to Marina for her role – as the criminals dare not interfere with him. His wife truly is his protector. Marina has long black flowing hair, cascading over her zipped leather jacket that is tailored smartly at the waist, and that has a turned-up collar. The zip is down, revealing a thin white and blue-striped cotton T-shirt, held close beneath her slim, unsupported breasts. Her elasticated trousers cling to her shapely legs. Her lithe figure captures one's consciousness immediately – for here is not only an exquisitely beautiful Russian woman; but also an incredibly powerful athlete. Mark, in contrast, wears a thick green-blue wool jumper; overlaid by his father's old brown, buttoned leather gilet.

Away from business, away from survival in the Russian Federation, Marina has grown to be one with Mark; her soul circling his; her mind rhythms pulsing ever deeper into his brain waves; this happy union her clear intention, when she first learnt of this dashing young foreigner – single; with so much to offer Russia; whom she understood already to love her country's culture. And Mark, for his part, fell in love with Marina at first sight; without knowing anything of her intentions. In fact, the love between them was instantaneous; occurring during that initial, brief glance when they met at work on his first day in the office.

Eventually, the passage ends, but there is no opening anywhere till it turns sharp right where, a little further on, it ends in a pair of exceptionally grimy, thick plastic double-doors; the latter overlapping at their point of closure. The couple push roughly through, emerging into a ply-faced octagonal room – the hide. Inside, they can see the corners incline, turning upwards to come together to form the roof apex. The floor is hollow-sounding with partially-finished timbers; the smell is now more pleasant, offering them the scent of the Korean Pine-faced ply; the smell more pungent, like Cedar Wood. Six of the eight walls contain long openings, each framed with wire mesh inserts; and on another, there is a fire exit; the last contains the doors through which they entered. Mark moves swiftly to one of the wire-meshed openings on their left, quickly lifting the frame forward; clicking it into place to fix it open. Then he and Marina get out their binoculars, preparing to search for any sight of the cranes, as the birds move amongst the swamp lands before them.

Marina speaks with urgency. 'I want you inspired in your creative activities, Mister Boss Mark Shackleton. You must appreciate everything natural in Primorsky and learn about the wildlife that is still so abundant in this place. If you can absorb into your heart all that is wonderful and beautiful here, you will never ever risk launching into anything that is uninspired.'

'Well,' Mark replies, earnestly, 'I do that every time I look at, or contemplate, you, Marina. Coming here only emphasises everything that is beautiful about you.' Her husband is smiling and Marina embraces this compliment, reaching her arms under Mark's shirt, as the binoculars slip from his shoulders.

A little while later, Marina is telling Mark about the different species of crane they can see feeding over the wide Khanka-Ussuri Plain. They view the birds moving slowly amongst reeds, tufts of tall grass, clumps of willow and spindly birch; the white beads of the cranes' necks and heads nodding back and forth. To their left, where the river runs from the lake, reed-beds become prolific; tall stumpy alders adorning the periphery; a spinney of fine poplars form clear areas, beneath which a larger number of birds are now foraging. To their right, the distant music of crane calls is interrupted by a train rattling over the Trans-Siberian Railway; a far-distant sound, offering no visible contact, as it travels north into the Amur Valley and, from there, onwards to Moscow. The sky is a feint dusky blue with thin pale clouds stationary overhead; the sounds that arise enhance a deep repose through the breathing chords of a wide-ranging eternity. The couple's awareness of all this is heightened. But for the seemingly-interminable passageway that links them to the world of civilization whence they came, the pair are now marooned amongst the wild wetlands south of Lake Khanka.

It is amongst this isolation that their passions for each other mature. Huddled together close, as the cool wind from the lake brushes in dry litter, Mark fixes his binoculars on an approaching flock whose calls snap the stillness like the sound of cracked twigs. Marina's hand, meanwhile, reaches down under his shirt, as a flight of sixteen Siberian cranes fly in with legs lowered to prance stealthily over the damp marshland. The birds' angled wings are splayed wide, their wing tip feathers upturned to help manoeuvre them to a gentle touch down; composing together on landing; then concluding with a long tapering choral repertoire. Stretching their heads higher than the grassy mantle, the cranes entwine their sleek gait in subtle slow motion into the surrounding habitat; few – if any – other creatures can compare to the graceful poise and posture in which the cranes so excel. This fact is being noted by Mark, as Marina's hand reaches between his legs; and even more is it observed by Marina, who views the birds as something physical that she must emulate now with Mark.

At once, great stirrings occur within the widespread colonies. A swathe of white-napped cranes swing in from all directions, run over the ground into the receiving air, their toes stampeding against the puddled-sod, as they rise to settle far away. Another group of the same species find a space just fifty metres from the hide; descending gracefully, they gabble as if something is troubling them; their wings enfold majestically as a Field Marshal might fold his cape around himself; white necks crowned with red braid, denoting their high status.

After a while, the male and female birds start their display – their heads thrown back, beaks searching the sky's zenith. Marina whispers as her hands rove gently over Mark's nakedness.

'The males are initiating a courtship dance; you see, they lift their wings high over their backs while they call; while the female keeps her wings folded by her side?'

The calls rebound between male and female, fashioned into a woodwind tutti; the cranes bow their heads; then spring into the air that seems to hold them momentarily, before they slip back to the earth that they so easily use as a springboard for this alluring spectacle; wings floating up, then retracting again; alternate, one to the other, in full display mode.

Marina points out to Mark the rare, red-crowned cranes on their left. The birds take to the air, move round and return; floating, their white wings streaked with black on their trailing edges; their long black napes, with a shot of white at their heads, forming wondrous abstracts as they dissolve their schemata one to the other; contours and contrasts sliding melodiously as they drift into descent. Marina's voice becomes so sweet as she strokes Mark.

'Now isn't that just lovely? We would never see a sight like that, staying indoors or going to the opera; now would we, dearest?'

Suddenly, the flocks from the distance rise and call. At once, every crane is in the air; the sky shimmers with gangly birds, beating wings, trailing legs, alarm calls perchance shifting in patterns yet composed as a symphony of a thousand scatter, criss-crossing against the fading blue sky; they are away. Marina's voice is sharp.

An Amur leopard on the prowl, I shouldn't wonder.' Mark notices a movement about three hundred metres straight ahead. A sinuous shape shuffles swiftly through the grass, then vanishes; its curved back and tail noticeable for just a short moment, before disappearing again. 'Yes, I just caught sight of it too, Mark dearest.'

Mark reaches his hand under Marina's T-shirt, slipping it round to her waist. She reaches up on her toes with a sigh; a longing blends with the fine threads of fear that are surging through her. Alone together, and in haste, Mark moves his hand gently over the skin of her stomach, unzips her jacket, pushes her T-shirt higher to kiss her nipples softly; suggesting to her they will be safe together; yet he longs to hold her naked to him. They both are overcome with the act of delighting one another – but a sudden, wooden creaking from just outside the door interrupts them; causes them to look up. They both stop; eyes searching one another; their emotions a mix of astonishment and pleasure; fearing that someone might at any moment come bursting through the doors...

Somewhere across the plain – far out – Lake Khanka gifts sparkles of sunlight; beyond lies Northern China. Asia is interminable, so Mark thinks. He offers his thoughts to his beloved Marina, in praise and thankfulness for having brought him to this wonderful place. She looks at him with her dark eyes, her beautiful white face unusually solemn – but aware of her husband's desires and intentions.

Mark continues. 'Isn't Earth a supreme gift? We tame it with loving care.

Its creatures – humanity, too – deserve its gracious bounties. Its beauties are its eternity – if only it's well protected and cared for by us. So, there should then be no shortages. No shortages of anything whatever for anyone… should there, dearest Marina?' His little speech ends softly; thoughtfully.

Marina nods, offering him her unique smile of understanding and a look that suggests her longing to be close with him.

Mark closes the wire-framed opening before they return down the long, lonely passageway; both admitting to each other how isolated it feels along this route, as they purposely clump back towards Marina's car as darkness approaches. Holding hands, the pair imagine separately – though not admitting openly – their fear of hearing the soft patter of the lone Amur leopard as it treks the wooden causeway from the other end.

They reach the opening, appearing like the exit from a tunnel, and before them is the Mercedes. They are part way to it, when Marina turns to Mark with her cheeky, beckoning smile. Then, wrapping her arms and delicate fingers round his neck, she says, 'You wait till we are together, my *Shhcottish* laddie. I will practice all I've learnt this afternoon about courtship; so join with me… right?' She laughs with mock shame, till Mark explodes in a burst of tender laughter. Marina, in her black leather attire, directs her fists at Mark in mock battle; he catches the feigned blows in cupped, welcoming hands. As they laugh again, Mark closes with a kiss mounted sweetly on Marina's white nape. As they smile gently together, Marina suddenly tenses, crying out, 'Look! Paw marks round the car, see?'

'My God, we've been spied on, Marina! It can't be long since it passed!'

Marina bustles Mark into the back seat. He moves over as she enters, closing the door; her face offering Mark a broad grin.

'I dare that silly leopard to come back and scratch at the windscreen while we are together…'

Comings and Goings

Bill MacKenzie

'Is that you, Murdo?'

'No, Granddad, it's me, Paul.'

'Ah, Paul!' Angus waved his hand vaguely towards where he thought the chair was. 'I should have known it wasn't Murdo. I can hear poor Murdo puffing away as soon as he's in the door.'

'Didn't see him in the corridor,' Paul said as he sat beside the bed.

'Never mind Murdo, he'll turn up I hope. What news?'

'It's a boy,' Paul grinned and Angus could hear the grin in his voice.

'Man, that's great news,' Angus lay back on his pillow with a smile.

'Not an hour ago. Elspeth is that tired and the baby was whisked away so I dashed along to tell you.'

'No Grannies there?'

'They're on their way,' Paul laughed. 'Elspeth took us all by surprise.'

'She's all right?' Angus asked anxiously.

'Yes, yes, fine,' Paul assured. 'Very happy but very tired.'

'And the boy?'

'Yes, everything fine,' Paul grinned.

'Well I'm real pleased,' said Angus. 'It took you both so long I was thinking I wouldn't live long enough to be a great-granddad. Murdo is a granddad ten times over – maybe more; I doubt if he could give an accurate count himself.'

'We'll bring him along for you to see,' said Paul and added hastily, 'Er, we'll visit as soon as we can.'

'That will be grand,' said Angus. 'And *see* is fine, Paul. I have pictures in my mind, so I'm not like the poor souls who have never seen. You bring the baby along and I will see him. Have you thought of a name yet?'

'Elspeth is fond of *Dillon*, but I'm not sure.'

'Dillon?' Angus flinched. 'That's a funny choice. Dillon MacKay doesn't have much of a ring to it.'

'I was thinking of *Mark* or *Magnus*,' Paul explained. 'Like you say, a name is better with a ring to it.'

Angus nodded. 'Think on to when this lad is a grown man. Maybe he'll be a lawyer or a bank manager or even Prime Minister. A name like Dillon MacKay would be daft for a man in that position.'

'It's a popular name nowadays, Granddad,' Paul explained. 'There will be loads of grown-up Dillons when our chap is an adult.'

'Indeed, you are probably right,' Angus conceded. 'But you press for Magnus or Mark or whatever it was you said. But if Elspeth has her heart set on it, you will just have to bow to the inevitable.'

'It's not decided yet.' Paul sounded doubtful.

'Held this boy of yours yet?'

'Oh, yes,' Paul laughed out loud. 'I was that nervous but he was that light. It was marvellous.'

'I remember holding your Dad,' Angus said softly. 'I happened by good luck to be home on leave when he arrived. I could see then, of course. In fact, that was the only time I ever saw your Dad. But I have that picture up here,' he tapped his head. 'I can see him now. Tiny, but with a mop of black hair. Your fellow got hair?'

'Yes,' Paul sounded doubtful. 'At least, I think so. I think it was reddish.'

'That'll be Elspeth's side coming out,' Angus nodded. 'It will probably change anyway. And did you look at his hands?'

'His hands?'

'Obviously not,' Angus sighed. 'When you get back to the maternity ward, you get to that boy of yours and have a good look at his hands. I can see your father's hands now. Never mind looking at a baby's hair or face; you look at his hands and you will see a picture that will stay in your mind forever. The hands of a new baby are the most beautiful thing I've ever seen. Look at the nails. They're like tiny pearls. The fingers are so small but so, so perfect. When you are an old man lying on your deathbed, you will re-run the picture of your baby's hands and you will be filled with joy.'

'You're not on your deathbed,' Paul objected. 'They were talking about letting you home. You'll get better.'

'I might improve for a wee while right enough,' Angus smiled. 'I think though that recovery is not on the cards. But it would be nice to die at home.'

'I better be getting back.' Paul rose from the chair. 'We'll bring the wee fellow along as soon as we can.'

'That will be just grand. Are you expecting your Dad to come visiting tonight?'

'I expect he'll come with Mum. Don't worry, he'll come along and see you.'

'Give my love to Elspeth,' Angus said. 'And to my great-grandson.' Angus heard the door open.

'Here's Murdo coming along the corridor,' Paul said.

'That's good. I was worried about the lad. He's late and he didn't turn up last night.'

'I thought he came every night?' Paul said from the doorway.

'He does; but not last night.'

Angus heard Paul call a greeting to Murdo as the door swung closed.

Angus had known Murdo for a long time. In fact, he could not remember a time when he had not known Murdo. Their fathers had worked on the same farm and the boys had played together and gone to school together all through their childhood. Their parting came like so many others, when they went away to war. Angus had gone to Africa eventually and, in a squalid town in the sand, he had opened a wrecked door and felt the blast and saw the flash – and that was the last thing he was ever to see. Murdo had got a dream posting to the other side of the world and had not been in Singapore a month when the dream changed to a nightmare. 'Luck,' Murdo had said, but it was really, Angus knew, stubbornness and native cunning which had made him one of the few survivors of the Japanese hospitality.

They had both returned home as wrecks, but Murdo had recovered quickly. Angus would not regain his sight, so he set about rebuilding his life without it; and he and Murdo resumed their friendship.

Even now, with Angus rushed into the hospital, Murdo would not be parted and arrived in his own ambulance two days later, and took up residence in the ward just along the corridor. Angus was still wired up with drips and so on, but Murdo had regained some mobility and was able to visit. His *outing* he called it.

The door re-opened and Angus could hear the gasping breath.

'Murdo, lad, come and get the weight off your feet. You met Paul outside?' There was no answer. Murdo needed all his breath to get to the chair. 'He'll have told you his news?' Angus knew that Murdo would respond when he could. There was no hurry.

'Aye, indeed,' gasped Murdo. After a little pause he added, 'Great news.'

'He's that pleased with himself,' Angus chuckled. 'You'd think he was the first ever.'

'We were just the same,' said Murdo.

'They're thinking of calling the poor bairn *Dillon*.'

'Dillon's all right,' said Murdo. 'It's modern.'

'Dillon MacKay? It don't sound right.' Angus objected.

'You're old-fashioned,' Murdo teased. 'Kids get all sorts of weird and wonderful names these days. You don't get many Murdos or Anguses; they're old hat.'

'They're good names,' Angus protested.

'Indeed they are, but they're not modern. Names come and go. You remember old Morrison that lived at Rosebank? His name was Eberneezer. When we were kids, we thought it was funny but it was a popular name when old Morrison was born.'

'And Duncan's father out at Westreay,' Angus joined in with a laugh. 'He was called Nethaniel.'

'There you are then. There weren't any Eberneezers or Nethaniels in school with us. Fashions change. It's no good you worrying about it.'

'I'm not worrying. They can call the poor bairn anything they like.'

The room fell silent, save for the gasping breath of Murdo. Their visits were often thus. They could sustain a silence without concern. They felt no need to fill every moment with chatter. It was Angus who finally spoke.

'What did his nibs say today?'

'Och, what can the poor man say?' Murdo sighed. 'He tries to be cheerful and up-beat, but what can he say to someone like me?'

'Right enough,' Angus said sadly. 'But you sound quite chirpy. I heard you had a bad night.'

'Who told you that?'

'One of the lassies told me.'

'They should stick to being nurses,' Murdo snapped. 'They have no business discussing my problems with every Tom, Dick and Harry.'

'Calm yourself, Murdo,' Angus soothed. 'When you didn't turn up last night, it was natural that I asked how you were and the lassie told me. And she knows I'm not any Tom, Dick or Harry.'

'Sorry, Angus, I was dead-beat yesterday and I didn't get much sleep,' Murdo agreed. 'Yesterday was a bad day.'

'But you feel better today?' Angus encouraged.

'I'm fine,' Murdo replied briskly. 'I am not expecting miracles, so I'll take each day as it comes. What about yourself? Any plans for going mountaineering or scuba diving?'

Angus laughed.

Murdo could always bring a smile to his face. He recalled when Murdo came to give him a spin in his new car. 'What make is it?' Angus asked as they drove smoothly along. 'It's a Nissan,' said Murdo. 'A Nissan!' Angus had yelped. 'But that's a Japanese make.' Murdo just laughed. 'That's history,' he said. 'I hold no grudges.' Angus had been unusually angered by Murdo's reaction. 'Maybe,' he said, 'if you were blinded by the bastards, you wouldn't be so forgiving.' Murdo was silent for only a moment. 'If they had blinded me,' he said, 'you wouldn't catch me driving their bloody Nissan.'

'Paul is going to bring the new baby along when he gets a chance. I suppose it will be tomorrow but...' Angus stopped and cocked his head. He thought he had heard Murdo groan. 'Murdo!' he said urgently. The room was silent – totally silent. There was no gasping breath. 'Murdo!' Angus cried.

He heard the door open.

'Granddad,' Paul greeted, as he came in the door, his proud gaze set on the little bundle of white that lay in his arms. 'I've brought Murdo to see you. We've agreed *Murdo Mac...*'

He had raised his eyes from the baby and taken in the old man in the bed with tears on his cheeks, and old Murdo flopped in the chair with open, surprised eyes staring unseeingly at the ceiling.

'Murdo!' said Angus. But this time, it was not a cry – it was a sigh.

The Clipping

Elizabeth Whyte

Old men regale children with tales of youth,
'It's a young man's job.'
'Aye, it is that.'
Their aged backs, bent in agreement;
Like a sniper, the collie plays his stealthy game;
And, wide-eyed, his flock trail into the fank,
Bleating for the lost among them.
The dog's tongue lolls, pink and fresh like a strawberry.
The shearer moves with the shape of the ewe
In a clumsy dance;
Her udders are still soft with milk, and she is tossed aside in minutes
In favour of another apprehensive face.
Deft hands work the fleece,
Twisting and rolling, tucking up loose ends.
Lanolin-soft, they tug out the crusted droppings
And strap the wool bag full.
Bursts of chatter, laughing and swearing all at once.
Then silent concentration like a church congregation;
The shearer works steadily from his pulpit,
Preaching his quiet sermon.
At last he stretches his aching back
And downs his dram in one.
Hot water, hard yellow soap and the homely scratch of a newly-washed towel.
'It's a young man's job.'
'Aye, that it is.'

A Place I Really Love

Elizabeth Ross

With a sense of anticipation and some excitement, I boarded the *El Al* plane for Israel. It was my first time out of Scotland as well as my first experience of flying. There were thirty-one of us in the group, comprising Scots, Irish, English, one Australian and, although I didn't know any of them, I did know the leader and his wife.

The flight was quite an experience; as the plane was a 707, the passengers went walkabout, and there was a compartment where you could watch films. We seemed to get meals all the time and there were games and magazines; so we were well-occupied.

When we arrived at Tel Aviv airport and descended from the plane, the most wonderful light, fragrant perfume permeated the whole atmosphere and, on enquiring what it was, we were told *Orange Blossom*. I can still remember it and smell it after twenty years.

The first week we stayed in Jerusalem in an Arab hotel that was staffed by men. In the morning, we were awakened by the sound of the Moslem call to prayer. *Allah, Allah, Allah*, around 5am or the hour nearest to sunrise. The call was sounded every six hours, heard throughout the city. We did a tour every day to the biblical sites, such as the Garden of Gethsemane, the Mount of Olives, the Pool of Siloam, the Via Dolorosa, the Dome of the Rock, and Golgotha. It brought the Bible to life, but was also very emotional.

The old city of Jerusalem was fascinating, strange and unique. We saw humanity in all its forms, some of it very pitiful – children and adults limping around with maimed limbs, and beautiful dark-eyed children expert in the art of begging. The rich, sharp smell of spices pervaded the air, alongside the odour of many animals. Being an animal lover, I was rather upset at the treatment of their animals. They used donkeys to carry goods. We would see a little donkey practically hidden under a heavy load and the owner whipping it to make it move faster.

As the Arabs and the Jews don't mix, there was a piece of waste ground like no-man's land that divided the Arab port from the Jewish port of the city. The older Arab men tended to sit at street cafés, watching the world go by, while their women folk stayed at home. On one occasion in the old city, where the streets are very narrow and the buildings quite high, we were aware of a movement at an upstairs window and saw an Arab woman watching us from behind her veil. We gave her a wave and she did wave back.

As it was Easter time, there were services in the Roman Catholic and the Episcopalian churches. One evening, all who were interested met in the old Walled City where a priest from the Greek Orthodox Church read from the New Testament. Then a large group of people marched in silence in the dark, led by guides with storm lanterns, along the Via Dolorosa; the way on which Jesus carried his cross. At certain points, the English minister read from the Bible, until we eventually ended up at Gethsemane where he closed with prayer. That was a very moving experience.

For our second week, we travelled to Tiberius on the lake of Galilee, which is a Jewish town. We were told that we could relax as we would not be plagued by begging. We could understand why when we stayed in a Jewish hotel and met the people. The Jews tend to be rather a proud race and get the name of being very industrious and especially excellent business people. They gave us the impression that they were well-to-do.

We did a memorable trip on the Lake of Galilee and visited a Kibbutz. On another occasion, a few of us got up at around 4am and walked to the shore to see the sun rise over the Sea of Galilee, which can be spectacular – although it wasn't that particular morning. As we waited and the sky got light, we heard singing and saw fishermen returning in their boat with their catch. They greeted us with *Shalom*. On our way back to the hotel, a Jewish gentleman was opening up the Tabernacle and, when he saw us, he came and shook hands and invited us in. As we hadn't been able to go into a Tabernacle previously, because of the Passover services, we were very, very pleased to do so. We also visited Yad Vashem, the memorial – inside a building – to the Jews who died in the Holocaust, where a perpetual flame burns, and the name of every country who lost Jews is inscribed on a little plaque.

The weather, being very hot, added to our enjoyment and, although we didn't sunbathe, on a trip to the Dead Sea some of the group swam, while others – like me – floated happily. One or two women plastered themselves in the health-promoting black mud. We also dipped our feet in the Mediterranean Sea, the River Jordan and the Sea of Galilee.

On our two Sundays in Israel, we were able to attend church services. In Jerusalem, we went to an open-air service at the Garden Tomb, where we heard the glorious singing of a male-voice quartet. The Prime Minister of South Africa, being on holiday, also attended, accompanied by armed police. In Tiberias, we attended the Church of Scotland.

Easter, being Passover, is a Jewish holiday and the greeting is *Shalom*. As we left, it was with a feeling of nostalgia and a desire to return at some time to this mystic land of the East, with such a historical and Biblical heritage.

The Story of Mr Mole and Mr Mouse

Judy Maker

What a nice day, thought Mr Mole, as he looked out of his door; there was quite an autumn feel to it. *I'll soon be sweeping the leaves from my doorstep.* As he was admiring the gentle blue of the sky and noticed that the grass was beginning to look just a little bit tired, he saw young Mr Mouse coming down the road towards him. *Hmm, I wonder what he's up to; no good, judging by what the other people in Animal Village have been saying in the meeting place.*

It was a very happy little village, looked after by all the friends who lived there. These included Mr and Mrs Dormouse, Mr and Mrs Water Rat, a pair of very busy brother and sister Squirrels and a host of other country animals; all getting their homes ready for the cooler autumn days and the cold winter season ahead. Lots of food was being gathered from the fields and hedgerows, and warm straw and hay was being stored – ready for the time when the important things would be hard to find.

Mr Mouse was getting himself ready to tell Mr Mole what a sad time he was going through, and how his life was getting so hard; and how he really needed some help with all his problems. Telling the truth was something of a problem in itself – for he found it so much easier to tell a little lie to get what he wanted. *Work!* He was thinking. *Not if I can help it. Mr Mole helps everyone else all the time – so why not me?*

'Good day to you, Mr Mole,' he said, giving a nice polite bow. 'What pleasant weather we're having… but it is beginning to get a little bit damp, don't you think?'

'Yes,' came the reply, 'but quite normal at this time of year. Now, what can I do for you, young Mr Mouse?'

Right, thought Mr Mouse; *that started well. Now for the next bit.*

'It is so kind of you to ask. I have a real problem building a house for myself – as I just can't seem to get it right. Everything I've tried seems to go wrong and I don't know what to try next. I was wondering if you would let me have one of your spare rooms...' He looked at Mr Mole, thinking to himself, *I'll add a little bit more to make sure that I sound really desperate and in need of his help.* He bowed his head, then looked up and said, 'I'll be happy to do some work to pay for the room, Mr Mole.'

Mr Mole in turn looked at his young visitor and, being a very fair mole, decided to test the mouse and make the rent easy enough to get if he worked for it.

'Now, I will let you have a room and it will cost fifty worms a week. I'll include food for yourself, as well as a nice warm bed. So go away and think about it, then come back with your first week's rent – if you want to accept my offer.'

Mr Mouse walked away having second thoughts when he realised that he really would have to work for his room after all. He had hoped that it wouldn't cost him anything. *Oh no*, he thought, *worms are so horrible. They squirm and they wriggle, and they feel awful when you hold them. But I'll give it a try. You never know, I might be able to do it.*

The first place he thought of was the farm – lots of buckets and pieces of wood where the worms might live; and there was the hen house, too. *There are sure to be some in there,* he thought to himself. He tried all the buckets and all the wood heaps – but every time he looked, the worms had already gone! They'd heard his busy little footsteps coming. *Right – then it's the hen house. I know there will be some in there. And the chickens all chattering away will hide the sounds I make.*

Mr Mouse was looking so hard that he didn't realise the chickens had seen him and had called for Mr Rooster to come and chase him out of their house. They were afraid that he was after their eggs. Mr Mouse ran and ran, as quickly as he could – for he knew Mr Rooster was rather cross; and Mr Rooster had such long legs and wings... he was so very fast!

Mr Mouse managed to get away, though, and climbed up onto a wall to have a rest after his fright. He was so tired and felt very sad – as he really had tried to do some work. As he sat there feeling sorry for himself, a very pretty little lady mouse came by and stopped when she saw how sad he looked. She gazed up at him.

'Whatever is wrong, Mr Mouse? You look so unhappy and all alone. Is there anything I can help you with?'

Mr Mouse looked at her and felt a lovely warm feeling inside. She seemed so kind and caring, and was offering her help without a moment's thought.

'Hello, Miss Mouse. It's so nice of you to offer to help me but, to be truthful, I was trying to get a room because I couldn't be bothered to try to build a house for the winter. And I realise now that I was wrong...'

'Oh, young Mr Mouse... I don't know any mouse on Earth who can't build a house if he wants to. But, if we work together, it will be so much easier to do.'

So they worked together and built the finest house in the whole village. Mr Mouse did the heavy work and found that he really enjoyed it; and Miss Mouse looked after all the fine curtains and the decorating. As they stood back and saw their beautiful house, they felt very proud.

Mr Mouse looked at this little Miss beside him and said, 'Miss Mouse, will you marry me?' He was so delighted when she answered,

'Oh, yes, Mr Mouse! I will happily be your wife!'

A little while later, all their new friends in Animal Village went to the wedding and Mr Mole was the guest of honour. Mr Mole had always believed that young Mr Mouse would be a good member of the village – if he put his mind to it... because *any* mouse can build a home if he really wants to.

They all lived there for many generations and – who knows – maybe they live near you, too...

Twinned with Hell

Simon George

Twinned with Hell –

That's the welcome you got driving into Lower Whipplesham – just after the 30 speed limit, but before you reached the post office and the duck-pond opposite. In fact, the sign actually read *Twinned with Hellesdorf* – a small hamlet in eastern Germany – but the collision with the articulated lorry six days earlier had seen the nice, shiny gold-on-black lettering bent forcefully back on itself. So, for the time being, Hell it was – Whipplesham the temporary twin of Devilsville; at least, until the parish council got handyman Bert to sort it out for them.

They'd raised all the money for the sign themselves, thanks to the usual – bring and buys, scouts and guides washing cars, and cream teas at the village hall. They'd had to, you see. Because it wasn't a *proper* arrangement; and certainly not one sanctioned by those ever-so-important people who just have to approve such things. No, the idea for this twinning had been the brainchild of one Captain Richard Mortimer, RN (Retired), of The Old School House, Juniper Lane. Mortimer had found himself delayed at Charles de Gaulles airport. A casual remark to the man sitting next to him and, who'd have thought it, after a mutual – albeit, at times, bilingual – tirade against the inefficiencies of modern-day travel, the pair had discovered a shared interest in wading birds of northern Europe. Well, they'd exchanged contact details – never expecting the other to get in touch; but both had – their e-mails crossing through the digital ether that very same night.

And eighteen months later, the unofficial twinning had somehow just happened. Nothing overly-highbrow. There'd been the sign, of course; hand-painted by Bert. And he'd done his bit for recycling – *requisitioning* one of the county council's amenity-tip pointers... not many tourists going to miss that one. So, a quick rub-down with a file; a can of black spray paint; and some gold gloss borrowed from the primary school art-room and Bob – or, rather, Bert – was your uncle. They'd also put an announcement in the parish magazine – not front page, of course; that had had to be reserved for the all-important news that Meg Slocombe's *Winter Snowscape* had made it to the quarter-finals of TV's *Don't Just Sit There – Sit There and Paint!* And then, finally, in a gesture of yuletide goodwill, they'd had the most gifted children in the village paint a huge Christmas card to send to their Hellesdorfan counterparts. Granted, it hadn't been quite the success everyone had anticipated – the sticky-tape holding the various panels together had fallen seriously foul of the trade descriptions act; and then... well, poor little baby Jesus, he'd suffered an injury; a large, jagged crease running down his forehead; victim of multiple folding-wounds as they'd tried to cram him in the jiffy bag. But, that said, it had turned out fine in the end...

with January seeing a nice letter arrive, thanking the children for their fabulous painting of *Herr Potter*.

Ah, but that had all been distinctly small-fry.

They'd had to wait another six months... but then had come the *real* step forward; major progress in cementing Anglo-Teutonic relations. Momentous. Surpassing all their expectations. Putting them firmly on the international map. For the Hellesdorfans had suggested an exchange visit for some of the older children. Well, the good people of Whipplesham had thought it a terrific idea, but they'd also feared it would remain just that; a dream; forever out of reach – because, to find the necessary funding, they'd have to sell cream teas till the cows came home; not to mention roping every guide and scout in to washing the entire county's vehicles for at least the next decade. But all of that hadn't allowed for little old Mavis Dawson. Interfering busy-body in life; but revered benefactor in death. Maybe she'd just wanted a few extra mourners at her graveside – no matter it wasn't friendship brought them there – but she'd left a tidy sum of money to cover the proposed trip. So, twelve lucky souls would soon be off to Germany.

But first, the Hellesdorfans were coming to Whipplesham...

'Mum! Tell Hayley to get out of bed!'

'Hayley, get up, please! We'll be late otherwise!' came the accommodating shout from down in the kitchen.

Hayley just pulled a pillow over her head. Too early by far. Besides, it was Gemma who'd signed up for this. Not her.

'Mum!'

'Hayley – come on!'

'Oh, OK...' came the resigned mumble from underneath the pillow. Hayley pounded her fists on mattress, ratty from her lack of sleep.

As far as her sister, Gemma, was concerned, excitement wasn't the word. She was absolutely buzzing. 'Omigod, I just can't believe it... They're coming here... Today!' She gave a little squeal. 'Oh, it's going to be so good.' Hayley had finally surfaced, so Gemma seized the opportunity to get a second opinion. Walking over to the dressing table, she pulled her make-up bag from one of the drawers. 'What do you think – *Pretty Pastel* or *Pink Blush*?'

Hayley shook her head; pitying the poor deluded fool. 'He's not going to be interested in you – so it doesn't matter what colour you go for.'

He.

Kurt Rasche. Hunky chunky brother of Ute.

Hunky chunky Gemma's words. Hayley couldn't care less about Kurt. What annoyed her was that their own brother, Peter, was going to have to stay at granddads while Ute moved into his room. Hayley knew that Gemma was annoyed, too – annoyed that Kurt would be staying at Tim Steadman's house. Wouldn't do to have the boys sharing with the girls, though. There were rules about that sort of thing. But, then, Tim's house was only two minutes' away and Kurt would have to come round for Ute – so her sister would still have plenty of time to make her move…

Gemma tapped a lipstick on the table-top. She'd made her decision. 'I think… *Pink Blush*. Makes my lips fuller. Far more kissable.' She opened another draw; took out a small box. Green suede; that contained ear-rings. 'Hoops or pearls?' She asked, holding a golden hoop next to her lobe, and staring approvingly at her reflection in the mirror.

Just off to one side, Hayley's eyes stared vacantly back; boredom registering at the corner of her mouth as she tried to stifle a yawn. But she knew Gemma too well. Her sister wouldn't let up until she got an answer. And the one that she wanted to hear.

'Right…' she sighed hard, '… what were we thinking of wearing, then? T-shirt and jeans?'

'No way… it's got to be a mini-skirt,' Gemma replied matter-of-factly.

'*No way*, yourself! You tart! Do you think I'm going out with you looking like that?'

'*Hayley – paley; none of the boys look at you!*' Gemma retorted. Her favourite taunt from years back. She'd got the looks; Hayley the brains. But she was confident she knew who'd get further in life…

Hayley tightened her jaw and let the emotion wash over her. The memories still hurt. But she wasn't going to give Gemma the satisfaction of seeing her cry again. She just didn't see the point of all the make-up; dressing to distract from who you really were. Ultimately, people had to accept you for yourself. But Gemma, she was always buying some new beauty product. And the clothes. Don't even go there… She did like her sister's hair, though – the way the dark brown bob framed her pretty face. A far cry from her own tangled mess which, most days, she just tied up. Boys… no, her dreamy sister was welcome to them; in her opinion, they were just a total waste of time. Now, *she* meant to do *something* with her life; wanted to go on to read astro-physics at university. She suspected Gemma would be lucky even to get a job on a cosmetics counter in the high-street the way she was going. Mind you, she'd probably get herself a good discount on all that lippy…

Their bedroom highlighted their personal differences, too. They'd squabbled for years over the décor – until their father had reached the end of his tether. He'd actually come in one day with a ruler and run a line of gaffer-tape down the centre of the room. 'Enough!' he'd cautioned them. 'This is your half, Gemma; and this is yours, Hayley. Do whatever you want – but keep out of the other's!' So, Gemma's area had become a shrine to the latest boy-bands; while Hayley's had settled into something far more demure – ponies and horses slowly giving way to star-maps and pictures of Einstein.

Gemma was still waiting for an answer. 'Hoops?' she asked again.

Hayley decided to get her own back. 'No... I wouldn't wear the hoops.' And, even as Gemma was looking for the pearls, she continued, 'Better give the others a miss, too.' She could see Gemma's quizzical look, and drove home her advantage. 'They all make your ears look lop-sided...'

'You cow!'

'Truth hurts...'

'Oh, I hate you!' Gemma composed herself, then said quietly, but with an air of finality, 'Hoops, then...'

'Hunky chunky won't like them...'

Damn! Hayley hadn't meant to say that – but the words were out; the damage done.

A second later, Gemma was rebuking her. 'You've been reading my diary! You utter...'

'Girls, come on!' Their mother, calling up again from the kitchen.

'Just be a minute!' Hayley shouted back.

Gemma sighed, exasperated, 'you're just *unbelievable.*' It took several moments before her anger subsided. She placed the green suede box back in the drawer; made a point of closing it slowly; then said, 'it's because you're jealous...'

'*Jealous*? Of you? In your dreams! Jealous of hunky chunky Kurt? He's not exactly storm-trooper material, is he?' Again, Hayley instantly wished she could have taken the words back. She felt ashamed of herself for using such language. She, more than anyone, knew what it meant to be tolerant; to accept people for who – what – they were. But a little voice of anger, repressed for so long, gave her a prod; urged her to go for it. No point letting up now. So she did. 'Your blue-eyed boy... he looks like a werewolf... Have you seen those eye-brows?' Gemma had seen them alright – not in the flesh, but in the passport-sized photo that had been sent along with the joining instructions. 'God,' Hayley continued, 'you wouldn't want to meet him down a dark alley when there's a full moon...'

'They just add to his rugged charm...'

'You've been watching too many soaps.' Then Hayley muttered under her breath, 'No wonder they're saying we're twinned with Hell...'

'What?'

'Nothing.'

'I need you down here, now!' Their mother's patience was being sorely tested. 'We absolutely must be away by eleven.'

'Yeah, we're coming,' Gemma shouted back.

They couldn't afford to leave it any later than that. There was a thirty-mile drive ahead of them to the motorway services where, at midday, they'd be *rendez-vous*ing with the coach and picking up Kurt and Ute. Just an everyday, normal occurrence. Repeated many times over the years at different service stations the length and breadth of Britain, as wave after wave of exchange students arrived to stay with host families. Normal – for most people. But normal wasn't a word in Hayley and Gemma's dictionary. Never had been; and never would be.

Twinned with Hell Hayley had said.

And the truth of that would come back to haunt her – haunt Gemma, too – in ways they'd never yet dreamt of. For when they finally left their teenage years behind them, adulthood would bring its own unique challenges. There'd likely be feelings of frustration, anger, jealousy on both sides. When the realities, practicalities – and *impracticalities* – of their respective wants, wishes and desires would throw up all manner of complications. When their different personalities and competing egos would clash once and for all. Career choices; friends; lovers – these and every other aspect of their daily lives inextricably linked; diversely interwoven.

That's just how it would be. *Had* to be.

For Britain's longest-surviving, conjoined twins…

My Red Poppies

Marlene Cowie

My red poppies
As we sleep, they grow,
whilst Mother Earth cradles her Earth to sleep;
my red poppies.
These are not just any poppies
But Ben Bhraggie, will-o'-the-wisp poppies.
My red poppies
With quiet intent, their petals dropping,
they know fine we will all return
in the morning.
Can a poppy have
Steely intent?
Mine do.
I know for sure
I can count on
my red poppies.

Remembering 2050

Mary Black

I remember real grass and trees growing outside under the sky. Have I told you this before? Or was that your father? There was no dome then, and the sky changed colour according to the weather. Do you know about weather? Well, that changed too... according to the seasons. Must I explain seasons – or do they actually teach history nowadays? I know you've been in Lairg village dome all your life, but you must have wondered how it came to be; who built it, and what was there before?

My mother and father – that'll be your great-great-grandparents – had a hand in its construction. When I was little, we could still go outside... but then the air became so toxic we had to stay inside and manufacture our own atmosphere. It takes a huge amount of power. Everything here was created by man, not God; and, of course, you will want to know who or what God was... Some people maintain he was responsible for making the whole world. He was supposed to have done it in seven days. Our little village dome took a lot longer than that. Well, anyway, whoever was responsible for building Earth... mankind destroyed it. We'd had warnings, of course, about Armageddon and global warming – but we didn't pay attention until it was too late.

I wish you could see some of the things I saw back in 2050. There were proper horizons. You could see the sun or the moon and stars with the naked eye. Beautiful!

After the war, there was talk about moving us out to colonise other planets. It was scary to think about... but maybe some of those worlds still have their Gods. Anyway, we would probably have ruined them like we did our own. You would have loved the farms and crofts where animals grazed in pastures. Flowers were different then, too. There are nothing quite like wild flowers in their natural habitat...

Mind you, in 2050, we were quite thrilled with our new dome. It was the last word in technology, and much bigger than the one at Rosehall. There was no tunnel between the villages in those days, and we kept pretty much to ourselves. I know you've seen pictures of the past, but they can't begin to show the reality. Rivers, lochs and seas had all sorts of amazing creatures swimming in them... until we caught and ate them all. They tasted wonderful. We also had meat, vegetables and fruit. Those flavoured oils they give us now just don't stimulate the palate.

Your headmaster tells me he is trying to organise a field trip outside for the school if he can get the funding for safety suits, and I see you are already wearing fancy new treads instead of wheels. Just as well, because wheels couldn't cope with the terrain out there. You'll be visiting the forests. Have you seen the images on the viewing cube? It won't be the same as seeing real woods of oak, pine, birch and rowan, but I suppose the turbine forests have their own sort of appeal.

I'm feeling a bit run down now. Would you wheel me to my regenerating unit and plug me in? The mechanic says my casing and inner parts are just fine, but my bio-brain doesn't send the proper messages to my body any more… but, then, it is four hundred years old! I could have a memory-chip put into a mechanical brain, but I don't see the point.

Thank you, child. Now, you trundle off home…

Saturday at the Loch (The Magic of Migdale)

Simon George

Wind-whipped, white-tipped waters,
rippling round my feet;
gazing on a landscape –
unfolding – rich in history steeped.

Breeze-stirred Scots' pine branches,
swaying to and fro;
bending; yielding; pliant –
outwit their ventose foe.

Mist-swirled mountain ranges,
floating in the sky;
aeons endured with solidity – a permanence –
earth to heaven they tie.

Calm-filled, quiet moments,
our spirits soaring free;
happiness – uncomplicated; simple –
bonds firmly you and me…

Bread Pudding

W S MacKay

In a posh restaurant in the city, I was amused to see bread and butter pudding on the menu. To round off a pretty mediocre meal, I ordered some, and was presented with a plate of saps; as far removed from the pudding that my Granny used to make, as night is from day.

The memory of these far-off days, when I lived on a small island in the Shetlands, came flooding back. I wondered what Granny would think about the so-called *Taste of Scotland* that I had just been served – the cost of which was more than Granddad could earn in a year.

On the island where we lived, there were no shops; we only got bakers' bread at the weekends when our parents came home from the Mainland on Saturday, or if we got a visitor who brought a loaf as a token. Granny baked flour scones on the girdle every day; they were so tasty and, with so many growing boys to feed, no scone survived long enough to go into the pudding for the hens' meal.

There were only four houses on the island. Granny's, Uncle Tom's and two others – every one was related to us in some way or other. There were five boys of school age or younger and, all week, Granny looked after us; our fathers were at the fishing and our mothers were working on the Mainland. In the pecking order of this gang, I was the third oldest – beating my cousin, Len, by four days; his wee brother, Larry – eighteen months younger – became our dogsbody, having to do as we told him… or we would not let him play with us. The two other boys were years older that we were, so mostly kept to themselves.

The men – Granddad, my father, Uncle Tom and two older cousins – would take home with them the week's supply of groceries, butcher's meat and sweets, paraffin Tilly Mantels, fresh vegetables and any household goods Granny needed. The boat would be loaded down in the water.

Our family was all herring fishermen and, if they had a good week and the men had a wee dram and were in good humour, they would be singing out loud as they lay on the oars. Always there would be some small toy or game for us. On Saturday mornings, we would spend our time up on the brae, keeping a lookout for the boat.

Granny's house – it was always called Granny's house, never Granddad's house – was the nearest to the landing, so all the goods were left there until collected.

Granny's pudding was baked in a big white enamel pie-dish, which had been liberally greased with butter. Granny would cut the bread into thin slices. No sliced loaf in those days. She then let us trim the crusts; they went into the hens' bin. She would butter and cut the bread into small pieces, sprinkle it with cinnamon and nutmeg, beat up the eggs and milk; then layered-in bread, sultanas, raisins and a few cloves, some honey and golden syrup, and a good sprinkling of brown sugar. The egg mix always completely covered the bread.

All the time Granny was mixing and making the pudding, she would tell us of how she had met with the fairies out on the knoll. They had told her their secret pudding recipe; she could not pass it on to us but, if we kept very quiet and watched carefully, we might just see the magic happen. She had a variation of this story for all her baking and cooking. The whole pudding was then left to stand for what seemed like ages before it went into the oven, *to let it breathe*. When, at last, it was ready, it was truly a pudding that was fit to grace any table.

On the island, we lived in a world of fairies and Selkies – seal-people who could spirit the young away. One, Aillie could, as she chose, turn herself into a Scorrie to attack lambs; or into a beautiful girl to lure poor fishermen onto the rocks, from where she would take them for the Selkies. She lived in a Geuo on the only part of the island where there were dangerous cliffs. We boys were not afraid of the cliffs, but no way would we dare challenge Aillie.

It was usually every second weekend we had the pudding. This was alternated week-about with clootie dumpling, and was served at the ceilidh in the evening when Uncle Tom, Aunty Betty and my cousins would come over from their croft.

My parents did not live on the island. My father was a Scotsman who came up to act as mate on the drifter with Granddad, so we came north in the month of April each year and stayed until the boats came home from East Anglia late in the autumn.

My mother worked in *The Welcome*, a first-aid post and sanctuary for fishermen and fisher lassies – the girls who gutted and packed the herring. It was run by the church, in an effort to keep young lads out of the sheebeen. Lerwick, at that time, was a dry town. It was there that she met my dad. The church had an uphill struggle – then, just as now.

That was how Granny, all week during the summer, became the only adult living on and looking after the island. Not only did she have five boys to keep in line, sheep and lambs also had to be tended. We had two cows that had to be milked twice-daily; milk put in the cooler to collect the cream; the cream in the churn to be made into butter and crowdie. All water had to be drawn from the well at the bottom of the garden. The three youngest of us had to comb the beach for firewood or maybe a plank or packing-case; reusable timber was always a prize.

Granny allocated chores to each of us and, until they where finished, we were on probation; that is, a note would be written and put on the mantle shelf to be opened by our fathers when they came home. Needless to say, the notes would disappear before *The Yagger* came alongside the landing on Saturday.

War came to Europe in nineteen thirty-nine and a way of life was lost forever. A German mine washed ashore, close by the landing – one of those big round ones with spikes; the motion of the tide and waves pushed it against the rocks and it exploded. The landing was demolished; Granny's house was wrecked; all the windows were shattered; the gable end nearest to the explosion was split diagonally from the found to the corner of the eves, and the slates were blown off.

Granny was re-housed on the Mainland in a council house with hot and cold running water, flush toilet, a bath, electric light and shops just a stroll away – but all the time she spent there, she pined for her Burland. She never lived on the island again, but did visit frequently during the summer months to tend sheep and lambs.

When he retired, Granddad built a fine new bungalow high on the side of the hill. Granny could sit by the big bay window and look across to the island and, from the same window, watch the boats come and go at the harbour. Granddad asked Granny to choose the name of their new home. She called it *Peace Haven*.

Hard work; long hours; little pay – but they had contentment unknown in our so-busy, modern world. Hard work never did them any harm. Granddad lived until he was eighty-nine, and Granny was ninety-two when she passed away. Lived on her own and still had all her faculties right up to the end.

There are no families living on the island now. A central structure, supporting the two spans of a new bridge – built there, incorporating the stones of the four houses – link the larger island on the south side with the Mainland. The grandson of a cousin grazes some sheep there as a hobby; he has a *PhD* in Marine Biology and works for the World Food Organisation.

I sat staring at my half-empty plate; tears ran down my cheeks. I sensed that the other diners were watching me. I was amazed that such an insipid fare could bring on so great an attack of nostalgia. I dried my eyes; paid the bill; donated a handsome tip to the staff-box; thanked the girl at the cash desk for the after-dinner mint, a pan-drop wrapped in silver paper. As I unwrapped it, I smiled, remembering Granny's advice when I was given a dark-grey pan-drop by an old man at the peat bank. She whispered, 'Spit the first two mouthfuls out!'

I buttoned up my coat and headed out into the night; back into my world.

If a Job's Worth Doing

M A Rodger

The fifth day he gets home knackered, covered in fish scales and feathers.
  'Omelette for supper, darling?'
  'Fine, dear; anything but vegetable stew again.'
  'And apple pie.'
  There's something about apples – but he can't remember what.
  'You're working too hard, darling. Take tomorrow off.'
  'Impossible. Animals tomorrow... I know... I'll squeeze mankind in with the animals – and take Sunday off.'

Unchanging Story

M A Rodger

Jack ascended the hill, accompanied by Jillian. They were poorly equipped for such a challenging climb – no map, no compass; not even anything to drink – an obvious requirement during such hot weather. Jack's friends couldn't believe Jillian's story when she raised the alarm – but she was certain. He was dead. He'd tripped, fallen to his death. He'd kicked the bucket.

You Bet, Bet You!

M A Rodger

Okay, we've had a few – but this is plain stupid. Five hundred quid? For drinking a pint of water? Tap water? Served from the bar? Drunk quicker than he can retrieve the flag from the eighteenth green? Two hundred yards away? And bring it back to the bar?
  'You're on, *sucker*!'
  'Barman. A pint of boiling water for my companion.'

The Noisy Umbrella Spoke

M A Rodger

'I didn't sign up for this sort of treatment. My hinge is really chafing.'
    'Hush. You'll get us into trouble.'
    'We'll turn inside out! You mark my words. And, then… we'll buckle!'
    'Nonsense. Buckling's a myth.'
    'Oh yeah! It only takes one of us. Then we're *all* history.'
    '*Will you lot shut up!*'
    'See? Now she's annoyed.'
    'Sorry, Miss Poppins.'

Helping the Police with their Enquiries

M A Rodger

It seemed utterly incredible. The old lady was confessing that all ten of the missing persons had been killed and eaten by her pet Alsatian. And it looked such a friendly doggy, lying in front of the fire, its tail wagging.
    'Oh, yes, Constable. He's the gentlest of dogs – until I say the command.'
    'And what command is that, Madam?'

A Difference of Opinion

Elizabeth Whyte

(Act One – The Car)

Julie is driving her mother to Orchard View, a residential home for the elderly.

Julie: 'We're only going to have a look; you might change your mind when you see it.'
Mum: 'I won't.'
Julie: 'I hear it's very nice; you might be surprised.'
Mum: 'I'm 84 years old, Julie. There is nothing left on God's earth that is going to surprise me – apart from the fact that my own flesh and blood want to lock me up.'
Julie: 'It's not like that, Mum; you know we can't look after you.'
Mum: 'Can't – or *won't*? Who says I need looking after, anyway?'

Julie:	'The doctor; the social workers…'
Mum:	'What do they know?'
Julie:	'They have lots of experience in these kinds of things.'
Mum:	'Have they; have they, indeed? I've lived through a war, had four children – *FOUR* – bloody ungrateful ones, too.' *She pauses for a moment.* 'No-one helped *ME* when my parents got old; when your Dad buggered… I mean, when I lost your Dad. Had to work all hours; it wasn't easy for me, Julie. What do social workers know about that, with their big, floaty-skirts and their organic peanut butter?'
Julie:	'I'm not sure all social workers are like Siobhan. What was that about Dad?'
Mum:	'And that doctor… well, he should know better. Where he comes from, they look after their family – no matter how old and useless they are. You won't find *his* mother tossed aside like an old sock; oh, no!'
Julie:	'You're being very unfair, Mum.'
Mum:	'*Unfair*! You don't know the meaning of the word. Boil an onion instead of an egg, and suddenly you're a raving lunatic. I'm just an inconvenience to you all. Can you slow down a bit? My hernia is playing up. I've served my purpose, and now you want to throw away the key. Don't think I don't know what you're up to. Those brothers of yours, they just load the gun and let you fire it, don't they? They put you up to it; I've no doubt about that. Inherited that trait from your Father. Have you got a tissue?' *Mum begins to get emotional.*
Julie:	'In the glove compartment. Oh, Mum, don't cry! It's only a look; nothing set in stone… Anyway, it wasn't just the onion thing. I mean, there was the fire in the kitchen last month.'
Mum:	'Well, that was your Uncle Bert's fault.' *Mum blows her nose hard.*
Julie:	'Uncle Bert's been dead for ten years.'
Mum:	'Yes, I know that, dear; but if he hadn't used my chip-pan lid as a bird feeder, the curtains would never have dangled in and gone up like that.'
Julie:	'You shouldn't have been using that old thing anyway. What's wrong with the deep-fat fryer we bought you?'
Mum:	'It looks like something out of the NASA space-station; just sits there beeping at me. I don't like it – and it doesn't like me. Oh, you lot think I'm off my rocker, don't you?'
Julie:	'I never said that!'
Mum:	'It's not what you say, Julie; it's what you *don't* say. I know how your mind works. Your Father would turn in his grave if he knew what you were up to.'

Julie: 'I think Dad would be pleased that you were being looked after.'

Mum: 'Don't bring you Father into this. He's well out of it; selfish bastard!'

Julie: *'MUM!' Julie is horrified at her Mother's language.*

Mum: 'Well, it's true… swanning off to Blackpool like that with his floozy.' *The car comes to a screeching halt and both Julie and Mum lurch forward.* 'Ah, for crying out loud, Julie! If you stepped on those hooligans you call children as hard as you step on that brake, they wouldn't be running around the neighbourhood out of control…'

Julie: 'They're not *out of control*; they're just teenagers.'

Mum: 'Yes, well… they could do with a short back and sides, and a good kick up the arse. Why have we stopped?'

Julie: 'You told us Dad was *dead*! What are you saying… that he *left* us?'

Mum: 'That's right.' *Mum is defiant.* 'Left me with three screaming kids and a bellyful of good intentions.'

Julie: 'What do you mean?'

Mum: 'He'd already gone once… came back, crawling… begging for another chance. You were our last-ditch attempt at keeping the marriage together. He left again just before you were born.'

Julie: 'But… you just said he'd turn in his grave.'

Mum: 'Well, he's dead now, of course. About seven years, I think…'

Julie: 'Why did you have him back?'

Mum: 'Because I loved him.'

Julie: 'I can't believe you didn't tell us… we had a right to know.'

Mum: 'Don't talk to me about rights. I've got a *right* to live in my own home… but where am I going? Yes, that's it – to the last petrol station before Heaven!' *They sit in silence for a moment. Both hurt; and both angry; then, Mum softens.* 'Look, I didn't want him in your lives. He was no good… and he'd only have broken your hearts. I couldn't face that. It was easier to tell you that he didn't exist. Now, come on, love; are we going to get going or what?'

(Act Two – The Old People's Home)

Julie: 'What's that smell?'

Mum: 'That's the smell of human despair, Julie. Oh, look out… here comes Attila the Hun!'

Matron: 'Hello Ladies, how do you do? I'm Janice, the Matron here. Firstly, I must apologise for the smell; we've a new puppy – he's not quite house-trained yet. Look, there he is… Timmy! Timmy! Come here, boy!' *A Jack Russell puppy comes careering towards them along the corridor, with something in his mouth.*

Mum: 'Oh, he's lovely; look at him, Julie.'

Julie: 'I didn't realise there was a dog here. I'm not sure my Mother would like that.'

Mum: 'Nonsense – I love dogs.'

Matron: 'Timmy is very good for the residents; very therapeutic.'

Julie: 'That's an interesting smile he has there...'

Matron: 'Oh, Timmy... you naughty boy! Have you got Mrs Simkins' teeth gain? Leave. Leeeaaaave!' *The dog takes off down the corridor again.* 'Timmy... come back! Oh, dear! Not to worry... I think Mrs Simkins is on fluids at the moment, anyway; stroke of luck, eh? Now, let me show you around, Ladies. We'll start in the dining room. This is where the residents eat their meals or, if they prefer, they can eat in their rooms; but, we do encourage them to mingle. We also have shows here; and dances, cards *etc* – usually bridge but, occasionally, some residents play a hand of poker...' *She nudges Mum.*

Julie: 'So, you encourage gambling?'

Matron: 'Well, we encourage residents to feel at home. You'll see we have a mini-bar over in the corner...'

Julie: 'They are *allowed* alcohol?' *Julie is visibly shocked.*

Matron: 'In moderation, of course... they *are* adults.'

Julie: 'But doesn't it interfere with their medication?'

Matron: 'Not everyone at *Orchard View* is medicated. We try a more holistic approach – yoga, Reiki, and other alternative remedies. To the left is the smoking room... Mr Thomson, one of our longest residents, grows his own tobacco in the greenhouse. Many of the people here find it most beneficial. This is the main lounge... as you can see, we have Antonio in every week for salsa lessons. Isn't he divine? Very nice, Cynthia...' *She calls over to a small elderly woman wrapped in the arms of a tall Latin man.* 'I see you're getting those steps down to a fine art! Everyone has their own room, but we are not averse to having folks *share* from time to time... if you know what I mean.' *Winking at Mum, Matron shows them back to the front door.*

Julie: 'Thank you for showing us around, Matron; but I really need to get my mother home now...'

Matron: 'Very good; lovely to meet you.' *She shakes Mum's hand.* 'And please do call any time if you would like another look around. I do hope I'll hear from you...'

(Act Three – The Car)

Julie: 'It's a den of iniquity!'

Mum: 'Don't be so melodramatic, Julie.'

Julie: 'Well, you're not going *there*; absolutely no way...'

Mum:	'I quite liked it.'
Julie:	'I can't believe she lets them smoke cannabis…'
Mum:	'It has some wonderful pain-relieving properties, you know.'
Julie:	'Mum, it causes psychosis and any number of personality disorders…'
Mum:	'I hardly think that's a problem at my age.'
Julie:	'But… gambling… And did you see that man dancing… in those tight trousers, with his shirt unbuttoned to the waist? It was *indecent!*'
Mum:	'I know… wasn't it wonderful!'
Julie:	*'MUM!'*
Mum:	'For goodness' sake, girl; when *did* you become such a prude?'
Julie:	'When I saw my mother drooling over a half-dressed Italian, that's when!'
Mum:	'Well, it was your idea to put me in a home.'
Julie:	'Yes, but – '
Mum:	'No *buts*. It was *your* idea and I will admit that I *was* dead set against it… but, you know what? I think I'm warming to the idea!' *Mum settles into the car seat and smiles to herself…*

Tock Tick…

Simon George

Lives still safe; yet to be extinguished;
reputation fluid; yet to be distinguished.
Tipping-point, stable; yet to be reached;
belief systems, national; yet to be impeached.

Red, yellow, white or brown – not yet beaten black and blue;
stranded colours; wires entwined – not yet a day to rue.
Rewards not yet collected – no maidens for the few;
time still for talk; calm reason; to adopt a different view.

New history; new lessons – a new message for the young;
words chosen fairly; spoken wisely; no barrier the different tongue.
And a ladder of diplomacy; climbed slowly – rung by careful rung;
A song of harmony; of peace; of understanding…
our goal, surely, to hear it universally sung?

Andante

Mary Black

The fluting voice of a whale sang to the rhythm of the tide.

The girl on the rock joined in, adding melody to the susurrance of the waves that drew ever nearer, filling the inlet and surrounding her with adulation. Sleek heads with melting eyes bobbed on the surface; a rapt audience of seals, which she unwittingly entertained until the sea swallowed her rock. She slipped into the glassy depth, her hair floating.

Droplets from a sparse waterfall fell in dulcimer chimes on smooth stones in the freshwater pool where she rinsed away the sand and salt. She loved to curl her toes in wet sand and to feel velvet moss against her palms; but it was time to go.

The magic followed her up the steep rocky path. She paused to listen to the wind as it played a haunting organ recital among the caves. Plaintive gull-cries gave way to the serenade of the blackbird, and the breeze had followed her to strum through the trees as she walked in the wood. Inquisitive little creatures scuttled in the undergrowth making their familiar, comforting chittering sounds. Her pulse was a metronome to the music of life. On the pasture, ewes and their lambs sang to each other in major and minor.

Aeneas was waiting at the edge of the wood. He put his hands on her shoulder and leaned down to kiss her. She ran her hand through his silky hair and down his smooth jaw. Her heart sang with joy and wept with despair.

'I know that you love me,' he said, 'so why not marry me now?' His melodic voice made a lyric of the words. She felt his tears, as he pressed his cheek to hers.

'In a few more months, I will give you my answer. Please try to be patient.'

'I am trying – but the waiting is killing me.' He held her tightly and she returned his embrace. She loved him for sure. She even carried his child. The longing to tell him burned in her throat but, for the present, that secret had to be kept; and perhaps forever.

Her mother was waiting at the cottage door.

'You've been down the cliff path, haven't you?' she said, and there was the faintest hint of panic in her voice. 'You know I hate it when you go there. It's so dangerous. The sea took your father from me and now you taunt me with your wild wanderings, as if you are daring the sea to take you, too. Have you no thought for me?'

'I'm sorry, Mother. I can't explain it – except that the sea and the land hold different worlds for me and I don't know to which I belong... but it will all be clear in just a few more months. I promise you.'

'You talk in riddles, like your father. He never knew whether he was coming or going either.' She shook her head sorrowfully. 'What can you know *then* that you don't know now?'

Miranda could not answer and she clasped her hands together, feeling the stretch of the ever-increasing webbing between her fingers. It had been growing since she became pregnant. Was the child telling her that the way was already chosen? Or would its strong father exert sufficient loving power to keep them all together? Whatever her child needed to survive, she would provide – though her heart might break.

'Don't go down there again tomorrow,' her mother pleaded.

'I am safe,' Miranda replied. 'I am watched over.'

'Your father thought he was safe and watched over – but it was the guardians that took him.' Her sighing was like wavelets on shingle.

'Think of Aeneas. He loves you. Doesn't he deserve to be happy?'

'We must wait and see,' Miranda said; and the song in her heart was a dirge.

In the morning, she walked up the mountain slope. The grass was tufted beneath her feet. The air was full of the coconut smell of whin blossom, and the birds sang a psalm to the morning. The sun blazed through a gap in the clouds, spotlighting her with warmth. It followed her slim silhouette as she climbed. Grass and whin gave way to heather. The breeze rippled through it like a harp. She startled a grouse and an alarmed deer responded to its panicked fluttering by whistling a warning. The ground shook as the herd drummed southward. The going became steeper and soon she was slipping and sliding on scree. The breeze sharpened for a spell, then faded to chill stillness when the sun hid back among the clouds. She felt the damp mist against her face as it cloaked the mountain, and she placed her feet carefully; first, lightly testing the ground before weighting her step. A fulmar squawked and she heard it echo round a steep chasm, so she changed direction and descended gently. She heard the distant sea symphony once more and imagined a far horizon. Soon she was back in warm sunshine and came upon a sweet patch of grass that had been missed by sheep and deer. She lay down among scented violets; as contented as ever she was – even on her rock on the ocean. She stretched and rolled like a cat. I love this too, she thought. I could have all this and Aeneas. She felt a slight fluttering in her womb. It was the first ever movement from her baby. Had she communicated her joy to the child?

'You will love your father,' she told it, 'and he will love us, and never leave like my father did. We will be happy here. You will see.' The baby stretched, but she could not know its thoughts.

Her mother was cross with her again.

'If it isn't the sea, it's the mountain,' she said. 'Other people's children don't give them such grief – and their daughters aren't blind like mine.'

'Hush, mother. I was perfectly safe and I have a feeling that everything is going to be all right. I shall have the best of both worlds. My father and my cousins will look after us in the sea, and you and Aeneas will care for us on land; and I'm anything but helpless, you know.'

But her mother had latched on to one word.

Us.

'Who is this *us*?'

'I must speak to Aeneas, now,' Miranda said. 'I'll explain later.' But she had the feeling that little explanation was needed. Life was a joyful rhapsody.

The Crocus

W S Mackay

The North wind blew cold today,
summer seemed so far away,
with tear-filled eyes that could not focus,
'midst slush and snow I saw a crocus.

In land still held in frost's tight grip,
'neath sheltered trees allowed a slip,
with petals reaching for the sun,
it promised summer days to come.

This harbinger of spring so bold,
defying the warning of winters cold,
it caused my very heart to sing,
this early-warning flower to spring.

Grey skies were then a lighter hue,
with here and there a patch of blue,
the wind it lost its razor's edge –
God bless – the blossom in the hedge!

The Race

Marlene Cowie

Turquoise jade the sunlight
and night-time falls dark green,
in a land below the ocean
that few have ever seen.
But once I heard a story,
told by a friend who knew,
of quite an amazing adventure.
Well, I like to think it's true.
It was dreamed up by the crab,
as he lazed among some weed.
Turning to his dozing friends,
he said, 'I know just what we need.
Life down here's so cosy,
we've become a little stale.
We must have an adventure
and strike a different trail.
We'll make a race of it.
The Race from Here to There.
If no-one wins,' he shrugged,
'then no-one will really care.'
So everyone got ready
and planned things with great care.
The octopus did exercises,
whilst the mermaid combed her hair.
When everything was finished,
they met down by the wreck
where Organiser Crab was waiting,
with a whistle round his neck.
'Goodbye, farewell and lots of luck.'
Friends all waved them off.
But when they'd disappeared from sight,
Crab heard a tiny cough.
Little apologetic cough…
The smallest shyest shellfish
that you could ever find,
had been jostled by the whale
and so got left behind.
Crab hailed a passing starfish

and tied her on quite tight
and, with no more ado,
they, too, swam out of sight.
Night-time shadows came and went
as our friends raced ever on.
Their seabed patch was very quiet
because nearly everyone had gone.
There was a shiny, blue-backed porpoise
and a spiked anemone;
a green and playful turtle,
all racing below the sea.
There was a giant spouting whale
and a tiny sea horse, too.
They chased the speeding dolphin,
who was just a streak of blue.
As they swam on, their pace slowed down.
Ahead the winning post.
Then suddenly a storm blew up
and some were blown off course.
The dainty corn-haired mermaid
was exhausted by the waves.
She wearily sank down to rest
in an underwater cave.
She rubbed her aching eyes,
feeling gloomy and alone.
She rubbed her eyes again
and let out a squeal of pleasure.
Glinting in a corner,
she saw a horde of treasure.
Laden down with jewels,
feeling like a queen,
she hurried away to tell
of the wonders she had seen.
Then there was the dolphin.
He was very brave,
guiding an ocean liner
safely through the waves.
He nosed his way past rocks
and his dipping, flipping tail
helped the worried Captain
to steer through the heavy gale.
The passengers threw him titbits,

for they felt he was a friend
and he swam along beside them
until their journey's end.
But not everyone was lucky.
Some found the race too tough.
Before the storm was over
they felt they'd had enough.
The octopus went loopy
and did a little dance.
He thought that he had won,
But, in fact, he'd swum to France.
About this time, not far away,
upon a sandy shore
lay the little sea horse, stranded,
and feeling very sore.
The stormy wind died down.
The sun was peeking out.
as he closed his eyes to rest,
he heard a gleeful shout.
When he looked, to his surprise,
above him bending down,
was a friendly island boy
wearing flowers and a worried frown.
'Oh, look; he's hurt,' he cried,
as his friends came running near.
'We'll take you home,' he said,
'so go to sleep and never fear.'
The sea horse soon got well.
Every day was filled with joy
and the laughing, carefree children
loved their new-found toy.
Who really won that race
was never very clear,
but they had all tried something different
so it was neither Here nor There.

CONTRIBUTORS

Mary Black lives in beautiful Rosehall in Sutherland. She is 72 years old and is still waiting to be discovered.

Charlie Byron is an Edinburgh chiel, considered frugal in the extreme by his long-suffering spouse, Lily. He is considering the possibility of gradual detachment from all sensible, sensual pursuits that incur waste.

Lily Byron was born and brought up in Ardgay and, after leaving school, went to Edinburgh where she met her husband. She and her family moved north to her father's family home in Rosehall in 1975. She loves attending the Sutherland Writers' Group; not just for the encouragement she receives for her writing, but also for the enjoyment of listening to the stories and poems of the other members who are all such interesting people.

Marlene Cowie, born in Golspie, left to study at the University of Strathclyde. A chartered librarian, she has worked on a number of editing jobs – including *The Library of Congress Catalogue*, and *Polaris Code of Practice* – as well as for Haymarket Publishing. Now she has 'returned home', she enjoys the challenge of creating her dream garden, setting aside time to indulge in her love of painting, and, encouraged by friends at the Writers' Group, composing more of her distinctive and well-loved poetry.

Wendy Davies grew up in London, where she trained to be a nurse. She married, and brought up her family in Plymouth, Devon. Now living in the Highlands, she has retired from the Health Service – but still has just as many people to care about.

Simon George relocated to the Highlands in 2007 to secure a better work-life balance for himself and his family. Prior to that, he spent nearly twenty years working for the Home Office in London. Simon now seeks to divide his time between writing – he has recently completed his first novel, a psychological thriller entitled *Second Sight* – and helping people achieve their personal and professional goals through his hypnotherapy practice (www.highland-hypnotherapy.co.uk).

Harold Lane lives in Dornoch and has previously been involved in planning sustainable communities. As he approaches his 78th birthday, he believes mankind has passed a significant tipping-point – where food shortages, induced by rapid climate change, will now see the *status quo* alter. With the inevitable collapse of society, a new one necessarily must emerge. This is the concept behind the trilogy of novels on which Harold is currently working. Included here are two excerpts from that trilogy – *Quoyness Chambered Cairn* and *Sanctuary for Cranes*.

W S MacKay – to whom this book is dedicated – was born, and grew up, in Helmsdale; he spent some of his childhood in Hamnavoe, Shetland, and began primary school there. He worked at several jobs – fisherman, hairdresser and, for twenty years, in the oil industry before retiring in 2005. He took up writing after attending an evening class – and was a founder member of the Sutherland Writers' Group.

Bill MacKenzie lives in Brora. He was a contributor to the anthology, *A Sense of Place*, published by Waverley. A number of his stories can be read on the Shortbread Short Stories website (www.shortbreadstories.com). Two of his works, *The Getaway Driver* and *Eyes and Ears*, have been recorded professionally and can either be listened to on the site or downloaded for free.

Judy Maker came to live in Golspie six years ago and joined the Sutherland Writers' Group with the aim of discovering her true potential. Poetry has, temporarily, been put on the back-burner while she focusses her attention on writing her first novel, *Rooks' Hill* – an excerpt from which appears in this book. She has also written a number of short stories. What the future holds for Judy, only time will tell.

David McVey is from Kirkintilloch and has published nearly a hundred short stories.

M A Rodger is a member of Sutherland Writers' Group. Although he spends long periods in Golspie, he lives mainly in Poole, Dorset. He has been happily – and unprofitably – writing short stories since attending a course entitled *Writing for Pleasure and Profit*. Micro-stories – comprising exactly 60 words, excluding the title – are one of his specialities. Several examples of these have been included here.

Elizabeth Ross was born and brought up in the village of Lairg, where she has lived her entire life. She retired last year from running the family shoe shop, which has now closed. She continues to live in the adjoining house.

Lynn Whittington comes originally from Liverpool. She and her family followed their dream of living in the Highlands in 2001. However, work with the NHS has now taken Lynn to Aberdeen. She is still a keen and active member of the Sutherland Writers' Group, returning 'home' as often as possible. Having two grown-up children, she now has more time to devote to her writing – focussing both on short stories and a novel. Lynn's dream now is to return to live and write in the Highlands.

Elizabeth Whyte lives and works in the Dornoch area. She enjoys writing short stories and attends as many writers' workshops as time allows. She is a keen member of the Sutherland Writers' Group.